HANDBOOK FOR AUTHORS OF PAPERS IN THE JOURNALS OF

Ion-Molecule Reactions in the Gas Phase

58

Organic Pesticides in the Environment

60

Ordered Fluids and Liquid Crystals

63

THE JOURNAL OF ORGANIC CHEMISTRY

JUNE 1967

VOL. 32, NO. 6, PP. 1695-2046

6/32

CHEMICAL REVIEWS

JUNE 1967

VOL. 67, NO. 3, PP. 247-360

3/67

VOL. 6, NO. 2, PP. 161-320

VOL. 59, NO. 7

JOURNAL OF THE AMERICAN CHEMICAL SOCIETY • JUNE 21, 1967 • VOL. 89, NO. 13, PP. 3080-3334

INDUSTRIAL AND ENGINEERING CHEMISTRY

I&EC FUNDAMENTALS

MAY 1967 (QUARTERLY)

13/89

Journal of CHEMICAL and ENGINEERING DATA, Vol. 12, No. 2, APRIL 1967, pages 157-284

I&EC PROCESS DESIGN AND DEVELOPMENT

JULY 1967 (QUARTERLY)

VOL. 6, NO. 3, PP. 265-392

ENVIRONMENTAL SCIENCE AND TECHNOLOGY

ESTHAG

MAY 1967

VOL. 1, NO. 5, PP. 351-450

Biochemistry

6/6

Inorganic Chemistry

June 1967

6/6

JOURNAL OF MEDICINAL CHEMISTRY

I&EC PRODUCT RESEARCH AND DEVELOPMENT

JUNE 1967 (QUARTERLY)

VOL. 6, NO. 2, PP. 81-144

3/10

Vol. 6, No. 6, pp. 1071-1270

ANALYTICAL CHEMISTRY

JUNE 1967

VOL. 39, NO. 7, PP. 697-856

7

THE JOURNAL OF PHYSICAL CHEMISTRY

JUNE 1967

VOL. 71, NO. 7, PP. 1865-2180

7/71

handbook for authors

of papers in the journals of the American Chemical Society

AMERICAN CHEMICAL SOCIETY PUBLICATIONS

1155 Sixteenth Street, N.W., Washington, D.C. 20036

Published by American Chemical Society Publications
1155 Sixteenth Street, N.W., Washington, D. C. 20036

Richard L. Kenyon, Director of Publications

Joseph H. Kuney, Director of Business Operations,
Director of Publications Research

David E. Gushee, Publication Manager, Journals

First Edition

Copyright 1967 American Chemical Society Publications

Library of Congress Catalog Number 67-24404

Printed in the United States of America

Designed by Hubert W. Leckie

Production Supervision, Susan Lehmann

Price $2.00 per copy, bulk rates available on request from Special Issues Sales,
American Chemical Society, 1155 Sixteenth Street,N.W., Washington, D. C. 20036

Preface

A major goal of the American Chemical Society is to provide chemists and chemical engineers with journals in which they may publish the significant portions of their research. Editors and reviewers help to ensure the traditionally high standards of these journals. It is the obligation of the individual author, however, to submit manuscripts representative of his best efforts.

The purpose of this handbook is to help the author. Major aspects of manuscript preparation are covered, including specific parts of the text, preferred use of terms, illustrations, presentation of data, and typing of final copy. Although selected comments on common errors of usage, spelling, and style are included, this guide is not intended to teach the art of technical writing. A short bibliography is included for authors who may wish to consult one of the many excellent books available on the subject. The procedure for submitting manuscripts and the method followed by the editorial staff for reviewing and processing them are outlined briefly. An index and cross references in the text have been provided for quick reference.

Few of the rules contained in this handbook are inviolable. But supplemented by the specific instructions published in the individual journals, they should provide a useful guide to authors in the preparation of manuscripts which can be efficiently and rapidly published.

Revisions of this handbook will be made to keep pace with changes in documentation, editorial and publishing procedures, and as a result of suggestions from authors and users of this edition. Comments should be sent to the Publication Manager, Journals, at the American Chemical Society in Washington, D. C.

EDITORS, ACS Journals

Acknowledgments

In the preparation of this handbook we have referred to a number of printed sources, books, manuals, and periodicals which bear on style, technical writing, and publication, notably scientific. However, we have relied mainly on the experience and advice of numerous persons—authors, staff members, and other scientists particularly interested in the communication of technical information. They have patiently read manuscript and proofs, made a great many excellent suggestions, and offered helpful criticism. We acknowledge their assistance with gratitude.

Special thanks are due the journal Editors and their staffs, all of whom have given valuable time and consideration to the sections of this handbook relating to their journals, as well as to the whole text. We also are grateful to John S. Ball and Dr. Blaine C. McKusick, Chairmen of the ACS Council Committee on Publications during the period of gestation of the handbook, as well as to all the members of the Committee for their encouragement and advice. Also especially helpful were Dr. Charles R. Bertsch, Production Editor of the journals, Dr. Guy Waddington, Director of the National Academy of Sciences—National Research Council Office of Critical Tables, and Dr. W. J. Youden, Statistical Consultant with the National Bureau of Standards, for their contributions, respectively, to the sections on technical editing, symbols and units, and evaluation of data.

Special thanks also go to Dr. Frederick Greene, Editor of *The Journal of Organic Chemistry,* for assuming the burden of being the ultimate representative of all his editorial colleagues as the handbook neared completion, and to Richard H. Belknap whose initiative and special sense of stewardship, in his position as Assistant Director of Publications in the early phases of this effort, were instrumental in the organization of this project.

The major appreciation must go, however, to Mrs. Simone Kyropoulos of the ACS Publications staff for her painstaking management of the entire project from start to finish. It was she who coordinated the contributions of the persons already mentioned both with each other and with previously published style dictums. Considering the great number of variables, this was a formidable task. The writing is largely hers, as is the over-all outline and organization.

DAVID E. GUSHEE, Publication Manager, Journals.

Contents

I.

American Chemical Society Journals

Table I. Quantum Yields of Isomerization of 1,2 bis(9-anthryl)ethane. (Solvent--cyclohexane. λ--365 mµ)

[A],moles/li	[O_2],moles/li	t°C	φ
5.0×10^{-6}	2.0×10^{-4}	25	0.18
1.0×10^{-5}	2.0×10^{-4}	25	0.18
2.0×10^{-5}	2.0×10^{-4}	25	0.21
6.0×10^{-5}	2.0×10^{-4}	25	0.19
1.0×10^{-4}	2.0×10^{-4}	25	0.19
1.0×10^{-4}	2.0×10^{-4}	10	0.18
1.0×10^{-4}	2.0×10^{-4}	35	0.19
1.0×10^{-4}	2.0×10^{-4}	70	0.21
1.0×10^{-4}	$<10^{-6}$	25	0.26
1.0×10^{-4}	1.0×10^{-3}	25	0.17

Quantum yields for the back reaction, which are listed in Table II, were calculated from the steady-state compositions; they depend on the measured values of the extinction coefficients, the quantum yield of the forward reaction, and the assumption that this yield is the same for 365 and 254 mµ. Light of 254 mµ was used to produce the steady state. Effects of the reactant concentration, oxygen and temperature are similar to those observed for the forward reaction.

Table II. Steady-State Composition and Quantum Yields of the Reverse Isomerization (Solvent-cyclohexane. λ--254 mµ)

Initial Conc. [A]°,moles/li	[O_2],moles/li	T°C	Steady-State mole % of (I)	Quantum Yield
1.0×10^{-6}	2.0×10^{-4}	25	4.5	0.42
5.0×10^{-6}	2.0×10^{-4}	25	4.1	0.37
1.0×10^{-5}	2.0×10^{-4}	25	4.5	0.41
1.0×10^{-5}	2.0×10^{-4}	10	4.8	0.44
1.0×10^{-5}	2.0×10^{-4}	35	4.8	0.45
1.0×10^{-5}	2.0×10^{-4}	70	5.3	0.49
1.0×10^{-5}	$<10^{-6}$	25	5.4	0.51

Page of a typed manuscript as submitted to the Editor of the *Journal of the American Chemical Society*.

THIS GUIDE HAS BEEN PREPARED for those who plan to submit manuscripts to journals published by the American Chemical Society. A prospective contributor to one of these journals should also *consult recent issues of the particular journal* to familiarize himself with its content, its style, and the specific recommendations and criteria of its Editor. A brief outline of the scope of each journal follows.

ACCOUNTS OF CHEMICAL RESEARCH

This journal publishes concise, critical reviews of research areas currently under active investigation. Most articles are written by scientists personally contributing to the area reviewed. Reviews need not be comprehensive. Indeed, they may be concerned in large part with work in the author's own laboratory.

Most reviews are written in response to invitations issued by the Editor. First- and third-person nominations of prospective authors are welcomed; nominations should suggest the research area for review, and they should briefly summarize the prospective author's contributions to it. Unsolicited manuscripts are also considered for publication.

In addition to these short reviews, somewhat longer review articles dealing with scientific fields closely related to and bearing on chemistry, and reports on scientific meetings written by scientists working in the field concerned, are also published.

ADVANCES IN CHEMISTRY SERIES

This is a continuing series of books that provides an outlet for symposia that cannot be published together in the Society's journals. The same rigorous standards of acceptance and editing that apply to material published in the journals also apply to material published in the *Advances*.

Preliminary discussions with authors concerning suitability of papers for publication are handled either through the symposium chairman or on the initiative of the Editor.

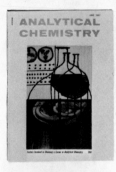

ANALYTICAL CHEMISTRY

This research journal is devoted to all branches of analytical chemistry. Research papers are either theoretical with regard to analysis or are reports of laboratory experiments that support, argue, refute, or extend established theory. Research papers may contribute to any of the phases of analytical operations, such as sampling, preliminary chemical reactions, separations, instrumentation, measurements, and data processing. They need not necessarily refer to existing or even potential analytical methods in themselves, but may be confined to the principles and methodology underlying such methods. Critical reviews of the literature, prepared by invitation, are published in April of each year in special issues which cover, on an alternating year basis, applied and fundamental aspects of analysis.

BIOCHEMISTRY

The aim of this journal is to publish the results of original research in all areas of biochemistry. Investigations that generate new concepts and experimental approaches are emphasized. Hence, the primary criterion in the acceptance of manuscripts is that they present new or germinal findings or concepts.

CHEMICAL REVIEWS

Articles published here are authoritative, critical, and comprehensive reviews of research, both theoretical and applied, in the various fields of chemistry. Preference is given to creative, critical reviews which lead to new chemical insight or new correlations. The subject of a review should be selected and the scope should be defined to provide unity of thought and logical arrangement of ideas.

Reviews are usually invited by the Editor as the result of suggestions from the scientific community. However, authors who wish to contribute an unsolicited paper to *Chemical Reviews* should contact the Editor for detailed instructions and suggestions before submitting a manuscript.

ENVIRONMENTAL SCIENCE AND TECHNOLOGY

This journal places special emphasis on reporting original chemical research, engineering developments, and technico-economic studies in fields of science directly related to man's environment. Contributed articles are directed to scientists and engineers concerned with fundamental and applied aspects of water, air, and waste chemistry. Because a meaningful approach to the management of environmental quality involves more than scientific understanding, the journal devotes serious attention to engineering, economic, legal, and other influences, to give its readers an integrated view of this complex system. Contributed papers should describe results of original research. Review articles are considered when they serve to provide new research approaches or stimulate further worthwhile research in a significant area. The journal also publishes communications and a correspondence section.

INDUSTRIAL AND ENGINEERING CHEMISTRY

This monthly journal publishes surveys, state-of-the-art articles, and critiques of current technology in applied chemistry and chemical engineering. Reports of original work are also published if they are of sufficiently broad interest. The objective of *Industrial and Engineering Chemistry* is

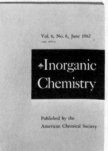

to aid the professional chemist and chemical engineer in maintaining and improving his competence by providing him with reviews that explain a subject and illustrate its utility in a problem-solving context without the necessity of detailed reading of the original literature, but with access to it through the bibliographies.

I&EC FUNDAMENTALS

Papers in the broad field of chemical engineering research are presented here. No technical field to which important contributions are being made is excluded—whether experimental or theoretical, mathematical or descriptive, chemical or physical. Acceptable papers are characterized by conclusions of some general significance, as distinguished from papers intended mainly to record data.

I&EC PROCESS DESIGN AND DEVELOPMENT

Reports of original work on design methods and concepts and their application to the development of processes and process equipment are published. Empirical or semitheoretical correlations of data, experimental determinations of design parameters, methods of integrating systems analysis and process control into process design and development, scale-up procedures, and other experimental process development techniques are included.

I&EC PRODUCT RESEARCH AND DEVELOPMENT

This journal publishes papers reporting findings on the preparation of new or improved chemical products, as well as findings on improved methods for the preparation of existing products. Contributions may also deal with new uses for existing products and findings on the modification of materials to satisfy the requirements of specific end uses.

INORGANIC CHEMISTRY

This journal publishes original studies, both experimental and theoretical, in all phases of inorganic chemistry. These include synthesis and properties of new compounds, quantitative studies regarding structure, and thermodynamics and kinetics of inorganic reactions. In addition to notes, a correspondence section publishes short letters of scientific merit reporting results or scientific views. It provides a medium for the informal exchange of ideas but not preliminary communication of results.

JOURNAL OF AGRICULTURAL AND FOOD CHEMISTRY

This journal publishes research findings from the several interrelated chemical fields closely associated with the production, processing, and utilization of foods, feeds, fibers, and forestry products. Topics most frequently discussed are pesticides, fertilizers, plant growth regulators, the chemistry of food processing, and the biochemistry of nutrition. The papers submitted should report original research, and some practical significance should be apparent.

JOURNAL OF THE AMERICAN CHEMICAL SOCIETY

Original papers in all fields of chemistry are published here. Emphasis is placed on fundamental chemistry. Papers of general interest are sought, either because of their appeal to readers in more than one specialty or

because they disclose findings of sufficient significance to command the interest of specialists in other fields. Communications and book reviews are also published. Specialized papers should be submitted to other journals of the Society.

JOURNAL OF CHEMICAL DOCUMENTATION

The advancement of the knowledge, science, and art of chemical documentation is the aim of this journal. Papers published cover all aspects of chemical documentation, including information services and sources, technical writing, linguistics, indexing and classification systems and philosophies, correlation and communication of information, and description and evaluation of new tools, equipment, and machines.

JOURNAL OF CHEMICAL AND ENGINEERING DATA

This journal is directed to the publication of experimental or, in some cases, derived data, in sufficient detail to form a working basis for applying the information to scientific or engineering objectives. Experimental methods should be referenced or described in enough detail to permit duplication of the data by others. The data should be presented with such precision that the results may be readily obtained within the stated limits of uncertainty of the experimental background. For most studies a tabular presentation or a mathematical description is preferred to the use of graphical methods.

JOURNAL OF MEDICINAL CHEMISTRY

In contrast to media devoted to organic chemistry *per se,* this journal publishes articles and notes on the chemistry of experimental or clinically useful therapeutic agents. The acceptability of articles is determined by the total significance of their chemical *and* biological data relative to the existing state of related information.

Types of papers considered for publication include those describing the preparation and physical properties, the structural elucidation, or the chemical behavior of materials of biological significance; structure-activity relationships; studies on drug dynamics such as those involving transport phenomena and metabolic transformations; and analyses of the mode of action of medicinal agents.

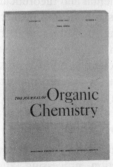

THE JOURNAL OF ORGANIC CHEMISTRY

Original significant contributions on research in organic chemistry are invited. Interpretive reviews of existing data that present new viewpoints are acceptable; mere compilations are not. This journal publishes notes as well as full-length articles.

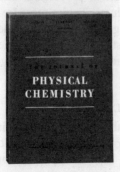

THE JOURNAL OF PHYSICAL CHEMISTRY

Original theoretical and experimental papers written for the specialist in physical chemistry are published in this journal. Preference is given to papers dealing with fundamental concepts, such as atomic and molecular phenomena or systems for which clearly defined models or definitions are forthcoming. Articles containing extensive reviews, reevaluations of existing data, applied chemical data, and papers dealing with measurements on materials of an ill-defined nature are, in general, not acceptable. Notes and communications are invited.

II.

The Scientific Paper

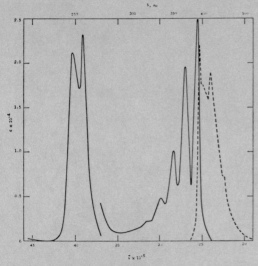

Figure 1. Absorption and emission spectra of 1,2-bis(9-anthryl)-ethane in cyclohexane. The scale for absorption between 220 and 270 mμ is reduced by a factor of 10. The emission spectrum is plotted as intensity in arbitrary units. It is corrected for variation of instrumental sensitivity with wavelength but not for reabsorption, which seriously distorts the curve at wavelengths shorter than 400 mμ. Absorption is indicated by a solid line, emission by a dash line.

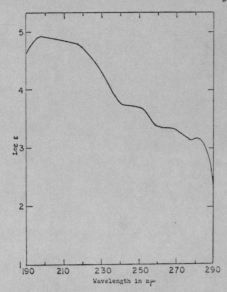

Figure 2. Absorption spectrum of the isomer (II) of 1,2-bis(9-anthryl)ethane in n-hexane.

subjected to flash illumination, under conditions which have been described elsewhere.[9] The maximum of this transient occurred at 445 mμ, about 15 mμ longer than the wavelength of the maximum of the anthracene triplet. The half-life of the transient was approximately 1.5×10^{-3} sec. An anthracene solution, prepared in a similar way, showed a half-life of 3.0×10^{-3} sec. These half-lives are minimum values and are probably much shorter than the values which correspond to the spontaneous unimolecular decay of the triplet state.[10] The observed difference between the values of the half-lives for anthracene and I is probably due to differences in the residual oxygen concentration in the two solutions.

Quantum yields of isomerization of I, in cyclohexane, are summarized in Table I. Generally similar results

were obtained using benzene as the solvent. Over a 20-fold range the yield is independent of the concentration of the reactant. The apparent dependence on temperature is of doubtful significance but, if real, corresponds to an energy of activation of about 400 cal/mole. Oxygen has a small but definite inhibiting effect. This effect cannot be explained as due to peroxide formation, since its occurrence would increase the apparent quantum yield of dimerization.

Quantum yields for the back reaction, which are listed in Table II, were calculated from the steady-state compositions; they depend on the measured values of the extinction coefficients, the quantum yield of the forward reaction, and the assumption that this yield is the same for 365 and 254 mμ. Light of 254 mμ was used to produce the steady state. Effects of the reactant concentration, oxygen, and temperature are similar to those observed for the forward reaction.

Table I. Quantum Yields of Isomerization of 1,2-Bis(9-anthryl)ethane[a]

[A], M	[O₂], M	Temp, °C	φ
5.0×10^{-6}	2.0×10^{-4}	25	0.18
1.0×10^{-5}	2.0×10^{-4}	25	0.18
2.0×10^{-5}	2.0×10^{-4}	25	0.21
6.0×10^{-5}	2.0×10^{-4}	25	0.19
1.0×10^{-4}	2.0×10^{-4}	25	0.19
1.0×10^{-4}	2.0×10^{-4}	10	0.18
1.0×10^{-4}	2.0×10^{-4}	35	0.19
1.0×10^{-4}	2.0×10^{-4}	70	0.21
1.0×10^{-4}	$<10^{-6}$	25	0.26
1.0×10^{-4}	1.0×10^{-3}	25	0.17

[a] Solvent, cyclohexane, λ 365 mμ.

Table II. Steady-State Composition and Quantum Yields of the Reverse Isomerization[a]

[A]⁰, M	[O₂], M	Temp, °C	Steady-state mole % of I	Quantum yield
1.0×10^{-6}	2.0×10^{-4}	25	4.5	0.42
5.0×10^{-6}	2.0×10^{-4}	25	4.1	0.37
1.0×10^{-5}	2.0×10^{-4}	25	4.5	0.41
1.0×10^{-5}	2.0×10^{-4}	10	4.8	0.44
1.0×10^{-5}	2.0×10^{-4}	35	4.8	0.45
1.0×10^{-5}	2.0×10^{-4}	70	5.3	0.49
1.0×10^{-5}	$<10^{-6}$	25	5.4	0.51

[a] Solvent, cyclohexane; λ 254 mμ.

(9) G. Jackson, R. Livingston, and A. Pugh, *Trans. Faraday Soc.*, **56**, 1635 (1960).
(10) R. Livingston and W. Ware, *J. Chem. Phys.*, **39**, 2593 (1963).

Discussion

The observation that the quantum yield of isomerization is not affected by a 20-fold change in the concentration of the reactant indicates that the reaction is a

The manuscript page illustrated on page 10 as it appeared in the journal.

THE PRIMARY REQUIREMENT of good technical writing is an effective and logical presentation. To achieve this goal, the writer must aim for accuracy, clarity, brevity, and consistency. Even in technical writing, however, where accuracy and clarity are paramount, a satisfying style—one that is not repetitious, monotonous, or dull—is desirable. Style and form in technical writing will depend on the material and on the writer's feeling for the English language.

The journals of the Society publish material covering a variety of subject matter. Authors, therefore, cannot be given a single set of precise rules to apply in the preparation of all manuscripts. It is possible, however, to state principles and offer suggestions which will help ensure a logical and clear presentation, whatever the nature of the manuscripts.

CATEGORIES

A prospective contributor to one of the journals should consult recent issues to determine the category into which his contribution might fall. The four major types of presentations that are published in the journals are articles, notes, communications, and reviews.

ARTICLES (published in all the journals except *Accounts of Chemical Research* and *Chemical Reviews* which publish reviews exclusively)

Definitive accounts of significant, completed studies should be submitted as articles. They should present new important data or provide a fresh approach to an established subject.

The organization and the length of these contributions are determined largely by the data to be presented. A single outline cannot possibly serve for all manuscripts. A standard pattern, however, applicable to many technical papers other than reviews, may be followed (see pp 19-25).

NOTES (published in *Analytical Chemistry, Inorganic Chemistry,* the *Journal of Medicinal Chemistry, The Journal of Organic Chemistry,* and *The Journal of Physical Chemistry*)

These contributions are shorter than articles. The material reported must be definitive and may not be republished elsewhere. However, the information is frequently limited. In some instances, development of a technique can best be described in a note. Notes are distinguished formally from articles by the absence of an abstract, but they are subjected to the same editorial appraisal as full-length articles.

COMMUNICATIONS (published in *Environmental Science and Technology, I&EC Fundamentals, I&EC Process Design and Development,* the *Journal of Agricultural and Food Chemistry,* the *Journal of the American Chemical Society,* and *The Journal of Physical Chemistry*)

These are preliminary reports of special significance and urgency that are given expedited publication.* They will be accepted if in the opinion of the Editors their publication will be of real service to chemistry. They should not exceed 1000 words, yet they must contain specific results in support of their conclusions. Polemics should be avoided and nonessential experimental details should be omitted. Communications are submitted to reviewers and they are not accepted if in the opinion of the Editor the principal content has received prior publication or publicity elsewhere. The same rigorous standards of acceptance that apply to full-length articles also apply to communications. These contributions differ from articles and notes in that the authors are expected to publish complete details, not necessarily in the same journal, after their communications have appeared. Acceptance of a communication, however, does not guarantee that the more detailed manuscript will be accepted.

REVIEWS (published in *Accounts of Chemical Research, Analytical Chemistry, Chemical Reviews, Environmental Science and Technology,* and *Industrial and Engineering Chemistry*)

Reviews integrate and correlate results from numerous articles and notes which are relevant to the subject under review. They seldom report new experimental findings. Effective review articles have a well-defined theme, are usually critical, and may present novel theoretical interpretations. Ordinarily they do not give experimental detail, but in special cases (as when a technique is of central interest) experimental procedures may be included. An important function of reviews is to serve as a guide to the original literature; for this reason adequacy of bibliographical citation is very important.

The character and scope of reviews vary considerably from journal to journal. The foregoing statements concerning individual American Chemical Society journals indicate the type of review each publishes (see Section I).

In addition to these types of presentation the following sections deserve special mention:

---

*Although *Biochemistry* does not publish preliminary communications, the processing of shorter papers dealing with important and timely observations is accelerated so that they may be published within two months or less after acceptance.

"Correspondence" in *Analytical Chemistry* consists of brief disclosures of special significance, reports of work which the authors do not plan to continue, or exchanges of views among authors.

"Correspondence" in *Environmental Science and Technology, I&EC Fundamentals, I&EC Process Design and Development,* and *I&EC Product Research and Development* consists of short contributions relating to previously published articles and presenting either alternative interpretations or additional data of interest. These contributions are reviewed by the author of the original publication who is given the opportunity to publish simultaneous correspondence if he wishes.

"Correspondence" in *Inorganic Chemistry* consists of short letters reporting results or scientific views.

"Aids for Analytical Chemists" in *Analytical Chemistry* are brief descriptions of novel apparatus or techniques.

"Experimental Technique" in *I&EC Fundamentals* includes descriptions of novel apparatus, instruments, procedures, or methods of laboratory observation and measurement designed for laboratory research. Experimental results or theoretical interpretation are accepted only to support the value or the accuracy of the experimental method itself. Descriptions of commercial instruments are not suitable, and discussions of well known procedures are included only if they make substantial contributions to new, inventive uses of the older methods.

"New Compounds" in the *Journal of Medicinal Chemistry* are short descriptions of the preparation and properties of compounds of potential medicinal interest for which biological or biochemical data are not available.

Some of the journals also publish special features such as book reviews, news items, letters to the Editor (see chart insert).

ORGANIZATION

Logical organization of the material to be presented is of key importance. Thoughtful consideration of the subject and anticipation of the reader's needs and questions will usually indicate to the writer the type of organization required. Although variations from conventional form are permitted, certain elements are considered standard parts of the manuscript. The following suggestions are intended primarily for the preparation of full-length articles but are applicable to notes and communications with some modification. When several closely related manuscripts are in preparation at about the same time, it is advisable for these to be submitted simultaneously. This permits editors and reviewers to examine the manuscripts in an overall context and avoids the possibility of fragmentation of the work.

INTRODUCTORY
MATERIAL

Title—The title of a technical document should tell accurately and clearly what the document is about. Choose title terms that are as specific as the content and emphasis of the paper permit; for example, "a vanadium-iron alloy" would be better than "a magnetic alloy." Balance brevity against descriptive accuracy and completeness. A two- or three-word title may be too cryptic. On the other hand a 14- or 15-word title is probably unnecessarily long. Ideally, a title should be an ultrabrief abstract. An article entitled "Metallurgical Analysis" should have been "Simultaneous Spectrophotometric Determination of Iron and Chromium in Steel."

Symbols and formulas should be avoided in titles. It is preferable to spell out each term. To facilitate machine indexing and retrieval, whenever possible use words rather than expressions containing superscripts, subscripts, or other special notations.

By-line and Supplementary Information—Every manuscript should have a by-line consisting of the author's first name, initials, and surname. In some journals the name of the institution and the city in which the study was conducted are also included. In other journals this information is given as a footnote to the title.

Even if the manuscript itself has been written by one person, the names of those who have contributed essential portions of the work are usually listed as authors. Correspondence and reprint requests will most likely be directed to the first named author unless otherwise indicated by a footnote. If the present affiliation of the author to whom correspondence should be directed is different from that held when the work was done, the new address should be given in a footnote. New addresses for co-authors are not, however, published in all of the journals.

Abstract—Every article must be accompanied by an informative abstract that summarizes the principal findings of the work reported in the paper. Although usually read first, the abstract should be written last to ensure that it reflects accurately the content of the paper.

Through a cooperative effort between the primary publications of the American Chemical Society and the Chemical Abstracts Service, a drastic reduction in the time lag between journal publication and abstract publication in *Chemical Abstracts* is taking place. This is being accomplished through the direct use by *Chemical Abstracts* of the abstracts submitted with the original papers. In a majority of the cases, the abstract is being processed for publication in *Chemical Abstracts* at the same time that the original article manuscript is in press.

For this effort to achieve maximum success, it is essential that the author be aware of the new importance taken on by his abstract. The ideal abstract will state briefly the problem, or the purpose of the research when that information is not adequately contained in the title, indicate the theoretical or experimental plan used, accurately summarize the principal findings, and point out major conclusions. The author should keep in mind the purpose of the abstract, which is to allow the reader to determine what kind of information is in a given paper and to point out key features for use in indexing and eventual retrieval. It is never intended that the abstract substitute for the original article, but it must contain sufficient information to allow a reader to ascertain his interest. The abstract should provide adequate data for the generation of index entries concerning the kind of information present and key compounds.

The abstract should be concise. Only in unusual cases should it contain more than 200 words. The nomenclature used should be meaningful; that is, standard systematic nomenclature should be used where specificity and complexity require, or "trivial" nomenclature where this will adequately and unambiguously define a well-established compound. References to numbered figures, tables, or structures presented in the body of the paper may be made in the abstract because these may readily be incorporated when the abstract is used in *Chemical Abstracts* (see Figures 1 and 2).

Hydrolysis of Phostonates[1,2]

Anatol Eberhard and F. H. Westheimer

*Contribution from the James Bryant Conant Laboratory
of Harvard University, Cambridge, Massachusetts.
Received September 29, 1964*

Abstract: A five-membered cyclic ester of a phosphonic acid, lithium propylphostonate (**1**), and a six-membered analog, lithium butylphostonate (**2**), have been synthesized. The rates of hydrolysis of these compounds, relative to that of sodium ethyl ethylphosphonate (sometimes compared directly, sometimes extrapolated to 75°) in acid are $5 \times 10^4 : 3 : 1$, and in alkali are $6 \times 10^6 : 24 : 1$. Tracer methods with ^{18}O show that the phostonates are cleaved at the P–O bond, whereas the hydrolysis of the open-chain phosphonate occurs with about half P–O and half C–O fission. The relative rates of hydrolysis at phosphorus are then slightly more favorable to the phostonates than the figures shown above. The previously established extraordinary reactivity of cyclic five-membered esters of phosphoric acid is thus paralleled by that of the cyclic phosphonates.

The extraordinarily large rates of hydrolysis of five-membered cyclic esters of phosphoric acid,[3] as compared to those of the six-membered cyclic esters,[4] or of the corresponding open-chain compounds stimulated an investigation of the properties of the corresponding phosphonates. The dilithium salt of 3-bromopropylphosphonic acid was cyclized to the phostonate, by internal displacement. Similar reaction led to the

FIGURE 1.—Example of an abstract as published in the *Journal of the American Chemical Society* and, to the right, as published in *Chemical Abstracts*. Note the handling of references to structures.

Hydrolysis of phostonates. Anatol Eberhard and F. H. Westheimer (Harvard Univ.). *J. Am. Chem. Soc.* **87**(2), 253–60(1965)(Eng). A 5-membered cyclic ester of a phosphonic acid, Li propylphostonate (**I**), and a 6-membered analog, Li butylphostonate (**II**), have been synthesized. The rates of

hydrolysis of these compds., relative to that of Na Et ethylphosphonate (sometimes compared directly, sometimes extrapolated to 75°) in acid are $5 \times 10^4 : 3 : 1$, and in alkali are $6 \times 10^6 : 24 : 1$. Tracer methods with ^{18}O show that the phostonates are cleaved at the P–O bond, whereas the hydrolysis of the open-chain phosphonate occurs with about half P–O and half C–O fission. The relative rates of hydrolysis at P are then slightly more favorable to the phostonates than the figures shown above. The previously established extraordinary reactivity of cyclic 5-membered esters of phosphoric acid is thus paralleled by that of the cyclic phosphonates.　　　RCJC

Reaction of Aryl Ketones with Cyclopentadienyl Sodium.
Syntheses of Fulvenylmethanols

R. J. Mohrbacher, V. Paragamian, E. L. Carson, B. M. Puma, C. R. Rasmussen,
J. A. Meschino, and G. I. Poos

Department of Chemical Research, McNeil Laboratories, Inc., Fort Washington, Pennsylvania

Received January 4, 1966

The reaction of 2-benzoylpyridine with cyclopentadienyl sodium in alcohol can be directed to give the expected 6-phenyl-6-(2-pyridyl)fulvene (3) as its dimer in 88% yield or the novel α-phenyl-α-[6-phenyl-6-(2-pyridyl)-2-fulvenyl]-2-pyridinemethanol (4) in 86% yield by varying the conditions. The reaction conditions which favor formation of 3 or 4 are discussed in terms of a mechanism for their formation. A variety of diaryl and alkyl aryl ketones, in which the aryl groups were phenyl, substituted phenyl, 2-, 3-, or 4-pyridyl, thienyl, or quinolyl, were allowed to react with cyclopentadienyl sodium. It was found that strongly electronegative aryl groups are required for conversion of diaryl ketones to 2-fulvenylmethanols. Aryl 2- (or 4-) pyridyl and di-2- (or 4-) pyridyl ketones form 2-fulvenylmethanols readily. Most diphenyl ketones do not form 2-fulvenylmethanols readily and alkyl pyridyl ketones give only trace amounts of fulvenylmethanols.

As part of our effort to synthesize 6,6-diarylfulvenes which are intermediates to bridged hydroisoindolines, 2-benzoylpyridine (1) was treated with cyclopentadienyl sodium (2) to give the anticipated 6-phenyl-6-... grated for one proton and (b) the higher melting isomer of 4 possesses the *cis* configuration.[6]

Early workers[7] had considered the possibility of ring-substituted fulvenes, such as 9, arising from reaction of...

CHART I

rapid dimerization to 7,[10] or an 86% yield of 2-fulvenylmethanol 4 (condition A). The product compo...

In terms of the mechanism, the results of var... the re... conditions (Table I) suggest that low... ...and concentr... ...ction med... ...dine...

FIGURE 2.—Example of a concise abstract as published in *The Journal of Organic Chemistry* and, to the right, as published in *Chemical Abstracts*.

Reaction of aryl ketones with cyclopentadienyl sodium. Syntheses of fulvenylmethanols. R. J. Mohrbacher, V. Paragamian, E. L. Carson, B. M. Puma, C. R. Rasmussen, J. A. Meschino, and G. I. Poos (Dept. of Chem. Res., McNeil Labs., Inc., Fort Washington, Pa.). *J. Org. Chem.* 31(7), 2149–59(1966) (Eng). The reaction of 2-benzoylpyridine with cyclopentadienylsodium in alc. can be directed to give the expected 6-phenyl-6-(2-pyridyl)fulvene (I) as its dimer in 88% yield or the novel α-phenyl-α-[6-phenyl-6-(2-pyridyl)-2-fulvenyl]-2-pyridinemethanol (II) in 86% yield by varying the conditions. The reaction conditions which favor formation of I or II are discussed in terms of

a mechanism for their formation. A variety of diaryl and alkyl aryl ketones, in which the aryl groups were Ph, substituted phenyl, 2-, 3-, or 4-pyridyl, thienyl, or quinolyl, were allowed to react with cyclopentadienylsodium. Strongly electroneg. aryl groups are required for conversion of diaryl ketones to 2-fulvenylmethanols. Aryl 2- (or 4-) pyridyl and di-2- (or 4-) pyridyl ketones form 2-fulvenylmethanols readily. Most diphenyl ketones do not form 2-fulvenylmethanols readily and alkyl pyridyl ketones give only trace amts. of fulvenylmethanols.

RCKF

VOL. 4, NO. 10, OCTOBER 1965

Dissociation and Reassociation of Rabbit Muscle Enolase*

Jack A. Winstead† and Finn Wold

ABSTRACT: When rabbit muscle enolase (mol wt 82,000) was exposed to 20% dioxane or 20% acetone in the presence of 0.2 M ammonium sulfate and 5 × 10^{-3} M Versene, a rapid dissociation to enzymatically inactive subunits of mol wt 39,000–44,000 was observed. In the absence of ammonium sulfate or Versene, or with magnesium added, the rate of dissociaton was greatly retarded. Upon dialysis, an enzymatically active dimer could be reformed in 45 and 87% yields, respectively, from the dioxane and the acetone system. High concentrations of ammonium sulfate alone also appeared to cause dissociation of rabbit muscle enolase. From the protein concentration dependence of the hydrodynamic parameters of the enzyme in 2 M ammonium sulfate, it is proposed that the process involves a dissociation, followed by unfolding or solvation, and finally a concentration-dependent association to higher molecular weight asymmetrical aggregates. It is also proposed that these aggregates of modified protein well may make up the crystalline form of the enzyme.

Subunit structure of proteins has recently received much attention both as a phenomenon with implications in biological control mechanisms and as an interesting problem in protein chemistry offering a convenient system for the stud... ...otein-protein inter-

found that dilute solutions of the enzyme were more stable in phosphate buffer than in imidazole buffer. Dioxane was freed of peroxides by passage through an alumina column. All reagents were of the highest chemical purit...

FIGURE 3.—Example of an informative abstract as published in *Biochemistry* and, to the right, as it appeared in *Chemical Abstracts*.

Dissociation and reassociation of rabbit muscle enolase. Jack A. Winstead and Finn Wold (Univ. of Illinois, Urbana). *Biochemistry* 4(10), 2145–58(1965)(Eng). When rabbit muscle enolase (mol. wt. 82,000) was exposed to 20% dioxane or 20% Me_2CO in the presence of $0.2M$ $(NH_4)_2SO_4$ and $5 \times 10^{-3}M$ Versene, a rapid dissocn. to enzymically inactive subunits of mol. wt. 39,000–44,000 was observed. In the absence of $(NH_4)_2SO_4$ or Versene, or with Mg added, the rate of dissocn. was greatly retarded. Upon dialysis, an enzymically active dimer could be reformed in 45 and 87% yields, resp., from the dioxane and the Me_2CO system. High concns. of $(NH_4)_2SO_4$ alone also appeared to cause dissocn. of rabbit muscle enolase. From the protein concn. dependence of the hydrodynamic parameters of the enzyme in $2M$ $(NH_4)_2SO_4$, it is proposed that the process involves a dissocn., followed by unfolding or solvation, and finally a concn. dependent assocn. to higher mol. wt. asym. aggregates. It is also proposed that these aggregates of modified protein well may make up the cryst. form of the enzyme.
RCCC

Chemical Abstracts indexing in the areas of synthetic and theoretical organic and inorganic chemistry is done from the original paper. For such papers the general content of the abstract should be as stated above, but the large number of compounds frequently encountered in papers in these areas precludes inclusion of all of them in the abstract. They are however included in the *Chemical Abstracts* index.

In general it is of utmost importance that abstracts be rich in indexable information to guide interested readers to the original paper.

The preceding examples illustrate useful, informative abstracts. The reader close to these topics knows at a glance whether the entire paper is of interest to him.

THE REPORT Although the different parts of the main body of the report need not be labeled as such and do not need to be in the sequence suggested here, they should include an introduction, an experimental section (*e.g.,* materials and methods) when pertinent, results, and a discussion.

The journals differ in their preferences for headings, and it is generally redundant to label the initial section "introduction." Theoretical reports may have a mathematical instead of an experimental section, or the equivalent of the latter may not occur at all.

Introduction—A good introduction states the problem clearly; it gives the background of the work and the approach of the author. Here the author should state the significance of his work in the context of what is known. He should orient the reader to the problem and should outline what has been done before by citing truly pertinent literature. However, a general survey of merely semirelevant literature should *not* be included.

Experimental Section—Enough detail should be given in this section so that other experienced workers familiar with the field could repeat the work.

(1) Materials used must be identified. Information on the degree of, and criteria for purity should be included. Reagents normally available in the laboratory should not be referenced.

(2) Apparatus should be described, *only if not standard,* with a drawing in specialized cases, and with names of specific equipment, and source, if not well known. Commercially available instruments should not be described.

(3) A description of how the work was done should be included. For experiments involving established procedures, references and characterization of the products [see (1) above] may suffice.

Any unexpected hazards encountered with the experimental work must be noted and emphasized.

The accuracy of primary measurements must be stated. For a guide to evaluation of data see Appendix 1. Theoretical reports should contain sufficient mathematical detail to enable derivations to be reproduced and numerical results to be checked. Also, all background data, equations, and formulas necessary to the argument should be included here. Formulas of all compounds, except those of common substances, should be given at least once, together with the appropriate chemical name.

Results and Discussion—For most papers the presentation of results and discussion of their significance may be separated into two distinct sections. Occasionally, however, a chronological approach may be preferable (*e.g.,* theoretical considerations followed by a set of experiments and a discussion of results that leads to a second set of experiments). Regardless of the outline followed by the author, the following points should be noted:

(1) Only relevant data should be included. Equations, figures, and tables should be introduced where necessary for *clarity and conciseness*. In general the same data should not be reported in both figures and tables.

(2) All numerical data should be reported in accepted systems of units (see Section III), and dimensions must be included.

In *Accounts of Chemical Research, Advances in Chemistry Series, Analytical Chemistry, Biochemistry, Chemical Reviews, Inorganic Chemistry,* the *Journal of the American Chemical Society,* the *Journal of Medicinal Chemistry, The Journal of Organic Chemistry,* and *The Journal of Physical Chemistry,* numerical data should be reported in the mass-length-time systems of dimensions—CGS (cm-g-sec) or MKSA (m-kg-sec-amp) systems and Celsius and Kelvin temperature scales (see p 45). The other journals do not require a particular set of units and dimensions, although *Environmental Science and Technology* prefers metric units. In journals of engineering interest such as *Industrial and Engineering Chemistry, I&EC Fundamentals, I&EC Process Design and Development, I&EC Product Research and Development,* and the *Journal of Chemical and Engineering Data,* data may be reported in the force-length-time and the force-mass-length-time systems of dimensions as well as in the mass-length-time system (see p 46). The author, however, must be self-consistent with regard to dimensions, and he must define clearly all units.

(3) In the discussion of the significance of the results, an objective explanation is essential. The features and limitations of the work should be pointed out, and the results should be interpreted, compared, and contrasted.

(4) A summary may add to the value of the presentation. It should be interpretive and not repetitious. The problem may not have been completely solved; if so, further study may be suggested.

Acknowledgments—Contributions of persons, other than coauthors, who have added substantially to the work may be acknowledged in a separate paragraph at the end of the paper. Supporting staff including draftsmen, machinists, and secretaries should not ordinarily be mentioned. Recognition of assistance should be stated as simply as possible.

Nontechnical information such as grant numbers and sponsors also should be included in a separate terminal paragraph or in a footnote.

References—Some of the journals publish references at the end of the paper; others treat them as footnotes (see pp 70-76). An attempt has been made to standardize as much as possible the format and content of references regardless of where they are situated in the journal.

III.

The Manuscript

Table I. Quantum Yields of Isomerization of 1,2-bis(9-anthryl)ethane
(Solvent cyclohexane; λ 365 mμ)

[A],	[O₂],	Temp °C	φ
5.0×10^{-6}	2.0×10^{-4}	25	0.18
1.0×10^{-5}	2.0×10^{-4}	25	0.18
2.0×10^{-5}	2.0×10^{-4}	25	0.21
6.0×10^{-5}	2.0×10^{-4}	25	0.19
1.0×10^{-4}	2.0×10^{-4}	25	0.19
1.0×10^{-4}	2.0×10^{-4}	10	0.18
1.0×10^{-4}	2.0×10^{-4}	35	0.19
1.0×10^{-4}	2.0×10^{-4}	70	0.21
1.0×10^{-4}	$<10^{-6}$	25	0.26
1.0×10^{-4}	1.0×10^{-3}	25	0.17

Quantum yields for the back reaction, which are listed in
Table II, were calculated from the steady-state compositions; they
depend on the measured values of the extinction coefficients, the
quantum yield of the forward reaction, and the assumption that this
yield is the same for 365 and 254 mμ. Light of 254 mμ was used to
produce the steady state. Effects of the reactant concentration,
oxygen and temperature are similar to those observed for the forward
reaction.

Table II. Steady-State Composition and Quantum Yields of the Reverse
Isomerization (Solvent cyclohexane; λ 254 mμ)

[A]⁰, m	[O₂], m	°C	Steady-state mole % of II	Quantum Yield
1.0×10^{-6}	2.0×10^{-4}	25	4.5	0.42
5.0×10^{-6}	2.0×10^{-4}	25	4.1	0.37
1.0×10^{-5}	2.0×10^{-4}	25	4.5	0.41
1.0×10^{-5}	2.0×10^{-4}	10	4.8	0.44
1.0×10^{-5}	2.0×10^{-4}	35	4.8	0.45
1.0×10^{-5}	2.0×10^{-4}	70	5.3	0.49
1.0×10^{-5}	$<10^{-6}$	25	5.4	0.51

Page of the typed manuscript, illustrated on page 10, after it has been checked by the Technical Editor.

THE READABILITY OF ANY JOURNAL is enhanced by consistency of format and style. This section presents details of manuscript preparation. Topics that are discussed include preferred spellings and punctuation usages, handling of words and numbers, conventions for abbreviations and symbols, nomenclature, preparation of tables and illustrations, format for documentation, and requirements for submission of final copy. The recommendations that follow are presented not to restrict unnecessarily the author's individuality but to provide general guidelines that will help him in his presentation. Many of the examples in this handbook are type-written to emphasize manuscript styles. Manuscripts prepared and sub-mitted according to editorial requirements can be reviewed and processed for publication more efficiently and rapidly.

The notes on style included here are not a complete treatment of the subject. They merely point out some of the recurring problems trouble-some to editors and authors. Most of the following suggestions apply to all the journals. In a few instances tradition of use has led to a somewhat different style for some aspects of manuscripts; we have attempted to point out these variations wherever they occur. *Authors should also consult current issues of the journal to which they will submit their manuscript to familiarize themselves with format, conventions, and details of style for that journal,* and then they should settle upon a consistent style for their manuscript.

SPELLING

Use American spelling rather than British, except in names and direct quotations. When in doubt, consult a dictionary. *Webster's New International Dictionary, Second Edition* is preferred; however if this edition is not available, the third may be used. In a few instances more than one spelling is commonly accepted for the same word; the author should choose one spelling and use it consistently throughout his paper. A list of preferred spelling for words and expressions often encountered in the journals is included in Appendix 5.

For accepted chemical terminology, in addition to the references on nomenclature (see pp 50-54), *The Condensed Chemical Dictionary, The Merck Index,* and the *Synthetic Organic Chemical Manufacturers Association (SOCMA) Handbook of Commercial Organic Chemical Names* are also recommended. *The Technical Speller* by G. G. Hawley and, for the spelling of trademarks, the *Thomas Register of American Manufacturers* may also be useful.*

Hyphens—Good usage sometimes sanctions more than one form in combining the elements of a compound word (two or more terms used to express a single idea). It is difficult to prescribe, for all circumstances, when to use a hyphen, when to write as one word, and when to write as separate words. Hyphens should be used only when necessary to ensure correct interpretation of intended meaning. For compound words in common usage follow the form used in *Webster's*. Several examples are also included in the preferred spelling list (Appendix 5). A few general rules are given here as guides:

(1) A compound word functioning as an adjective and placed *before* the noun it modifies is usually hyphenated.

a melting-point determination
a determination of melting point
a low-molecular-weight compound
a compound of low molecular weight

(2) The names of chemical compounds that are unhyphenated when used as nouns remain unhyphenated when used as adjectives.

a sodium chloride solution
a barium sulfate precipitate

Note: A dash, not a hyphen, is used between components of a mixed solvent.

The melting point was unchanged after three crystallizations from hexane—benzene.

(3) Hyphens are used to set apart numbers, Greek letters, configurational letters, and italicized prefixes in chemical names.

2-benzoylbenzoic acid, cholesterol α-oxide,
D-arabinose, *trans*-2-bromocyclopentanol

(4) Do not hyphenate adverb-adjective combinations.

accurately measured values
a carefully planned experiment

(5) When two or more unit modifiers have the same base, use a hyphen after each element dependent on that base.

25-, 50-, and 100-ml flasks
long- and short-term corrosion rates

The Condensed Chemical Dictionary, Reinhold Publishing Corp., New York, N.Y., 1961. *The Merck Index,* Merck Co., Inc., Rahway, N.J., 1960. *SOCMA Handbook of Commercial Organic Chemical Names,* Chemical Abstracts Service, American Chemical Society, Columbus, Ohio, 1965. *The Technical Speller,* G. G. Hawley and A. W. Hawley, Reinhold Publishing Corp., New York, N.Y., 1955. *Thomas Register of American Manufacturers,* Thomas Publishing Co., New York, N.Y., 1966.

(6) The following prefixes usually are *not* hyphenated:

after, anti, auto, co, de, down,
electro, infra, iso, metallo, mid,
macro, micro, non, over, physico,
poly, pre, post, photo, re, semi, sub,
stereo, up, un (except in the case of
un-ionized), ultra, visco

PUNCTUATION

For general rules of punctuation the author may wish to consult a handbook of English composition or a dictionary. Punctuation to be used in footnotes, references, abbreviations, and chemical and mathematical expressions should follow the usage recommended in the corresponding sections of this guide. The following suggestions should be especially noted:

(1) Do *not* use a period after symbols and most abbreviations.

(2) Punctuate all simple series with commas.

(3) Place a comma before "and" and "or" in a simple series.

(4) Do not use commas in writing numbers. A point is used for the decimal sign.

(5) Use a colon to separate parts of ratios.

(6) Use the sequence { [( )] } for signs of aggregation in chemical and mathematical expressions except where conventional notation specifies some other order.

(7) In manuscripts the dash should be typed as two hyphens, thus, - -.

HANDLING OF WORDS

Numerous authoritative texts on rhetoric, style, and grammar are available. A list of particularly valuable source books is included in this handbook. Authors may find the recommended references to language and technical writing useful as detailed guides to correct usage (see p 117).

In writing his report the author should strive for conciseness and clarity. Words and expressions should be chosen carefully to convey the correct meaning.

(1) Avoid introducing sentences by "it was found that" or "it was demonstrated that."

(2) Where directness is desired, use the active voice. Avoid passive constructions such as "is depended upon;" "depends on" is preferred.

(3) Avoid unnecessary words; logic prohibits such duplication as:

estimated at *about* 10%	*oval* in *shape*
such as copper, iron, *etc.*	they are *both alike*
bright *red* in *color*	*throughout the entire* experiment
fewer in *number*	*two equal halves*

Wordy expressions may often be substituted by a single word. For example:

owing to the fact that—because	by means of—by
subsequent to—after	it appears that—apparently
on the order of—about	of great importance—important
in the near future—soon	in consequence of this fact—therefore
at the present time—now	a very limited number of—few

Manuscripts must be free of grammatical errors. Certain faulty constructions or stylistic flaws are likely to be confusing. A list of terms commonly misused by writers and examples of constructions that offer special hazards are included in Appendix 6.

USE OF ITALICS

Italics help the reader quickly distinguish letters, words, or phrases from the rest of the text. All material that is to appear in italics when printed is underscored by a single straight line in the manuscript. Entries requiring boldface type are marked with a wavy underline; small capitals are indicated by underlining twice. Recommendations and specific examples regarding the conventional use of special type faces in the journals for abbreviations and symbols, in references, and in footnotes are included in the sections of the handbook pertinent to these subjects. *Authors must pay particular attention to the required use of italics in nomenclature and for symbols.*

The following rules should be noted:

(1) Italics may be used *sparingly* to emphasize a word or phrase; long passages should not be italicized.

(2) Foreign words and phrases (except titles and proper names) and several Latin expressions and abbreviations, such as *ca., vs., et al., i.e., e.g.,* in common use in English writing should be italicized; etc. is an exception and is not italicized.

(3) Chemical formulas are *not* italicized. Hyphenated prefixes to formulas, such as *cis-, trans-, o-, m-, p-,* however, should be underlined for italics in the manuscript, thus, cis-, trans-, o-, m-, p-.

(4) Greek letters and trigonometrical terms such as sin, tan, cos, log, mod, should *not* be underlined in the manuscript.

(5) The scientific names of genera, species, and varieties are italicized.

(6) References to the names of periodicals and their abbreviations must be in italics.

NUMBERS AND MATHEMATICAL EXPRESSIONS

The following rules represent accepted practice in writing numbers:

(1) Use figures for exact numbers above ten and spell out numbers below 11. Where several numbers, some above and some below ten, appear in the same passage, use figures exclusively.

five experiments

3 beakers and 12 test tubes

the 11th and 12th lines

the 2nd and 20th samples

the first and third equations

(2) Use figures for a number of technical units, as with units of measurement, whether below or above ten.

samples of 0.30 and 0.16 g

a 5-g sample

yields of 63--65%

a factor of 3

ratio of 2:3

heated for 6 hr

was tried at temperatures of 25 to 100°

(3) Use figures for numbers expressing a series. Never spell out dates or page numbers.

expt 12   pp 35--42   147--200°

(4) Use decimals rather than fractions for mixed numbers.

2.5 sec (not 2 1/2 sec)   5.25 g (not 5 1/4 g)

(5) Spell out the shorter or first number in writing compound number adjectives.

three 25-ml beakers   twelve 5-g samples

(6) Spell out numbers at the beginning of a sentence, or preferably recast the sentence to avoid putting numbers first.

Twenty slides were examined.

Fifty grams was treated.

or,

A 50-g sample was treated.

(7) Do not repeat the same number in both numerals and words; for example, do not write "a period of five (5) minutes."

(8) To keep the reader from the possibility of misreading, place a zero before the decimal point in writing numbers with no integer.

0.50   0.175

(9) In tables to facilitate the reading of *long numbers,* occasionally the digits should be arranged in *groups of three,* but *no* comma should be used. A point is used for the decimal sign.

0.8182   3 251 651

0.5749   3 259 509

0.004837   3 254 072

(10) Use of exponential numbers is encouraged where it will save space.

3.2×10^6 rather than   3 200 000

(11) Attention should be given to include the appropriate number of significant figures.

(12) When exponential powers of ten are used in designating the co-ordinates of graphs, it is preferable to place the exponential power of ten involved adjacent to the number rather than with the units in the titles or headings where confusion may readily occur.

(13) Numbers and mathematical expressions are subject to various rules and conventions for spacing and typesetting. Write

$(3.24 \pm 0.01)10^{12}$ $20 \pm 2\%$

25 g ($\pm 1\%$)   not $25 \pm 1\%$ g

(see also Hints to the Typist, p 101).

(14) Multiplication and division may be indicated in the following ways:

a multiplied by *b* $\underline{ab}$

a divided by *b* $\underline{a}/\underline{b}$, $\underline{ab}^{-1}$

$$\frac{a}{b}$$, in display equations only.

When the quantities being multiplied or divided are themselves products, quotients, sums, or differences of other quantities, parentheses must be used in accordance with the rules of mathematics.

If the solidus ($/$) is used in division and if there is any doubt where the numerator starts or where the denominator ends, parentheses should be used.

It is recommended that in expressions like

$$\sin \{2\pi(\underline{x} - \underline{x}_0)/\lambda\} \qquad \exp \{-V(\underline{r})/\underline{kT}\},$$

the argument should always be placed within braces, except when the argument is a simple product of two quantities:

e.g., $\sin \underline{kx}$

(15) Preferred style for mathematical expressions varies as follows:

for expressions in displayed equations	*for expressions in text*
$\dfrac{\underline{a}}{\underline{bcd}}$	$\underline{a}/\underline{bcd}$
$\dfrac{2}{9}\sin \underline{kx}, \ \dfrac{1}{2}\underline{RT}$	$(2/9)\sin \underline{kx}, \ (1/2)\underline{RT}$ or $\underline{RT}/2$
$\dfrac{\dfrac{\underline{a}}{\underline{b}}}{\underline{c}}$	$(\underline{a}/\underline{b}) - \underline{c}$
$\dfrac{\underline{a}}{\underline{b} - \underline{c}}$	$\underline{a}/(\underline{b} - \underline{c})$
$\dfrac{\underline{a} - \underline{b}}{\underline{c} - \underline{d}}$	$(\underline{a} - \underline{b})/(\underline{c} - \underline{d})$
$\dfrac{\underline{a}}{\underline{c}} - \dfrac{\underline{b}}{\underline{d}}$	$(\underline{a}/\underline{c}) - (\underline{b}/\underline{d})$

(16) A few examples of usages and symbols for mathematical operations and constants as they should appear in the manuscript are listed below (see also Hints to the Typist, p 101):

approximately equal to ..... $\approx$

proportional to .... $\propto$

approaches .... $\rightarrow$

absolute magnitude of *a* .... $|\underline{a}|$

square root of *a* .... $\sqrt{\underline{a}}, \ \underline{a}^{1/2}$

*n*th root of *a* .... $\sqrt[\underline{n}]{\underline{a}}, \ \underline{a}^{1/\underline{n}}$

mean value of *a* .... $\bar{\underline{a}}, \quad \langle \underline{a} \rangle$

logarithm to the base a of x .... $\log_a \underline{x}$

natural logarithm of x .... $\ln \underline{x}$

finite increment of x .... $\Delta\underline{x}$

infinitesimal increment of x .... $\delta\underline{x}$

total differential of x .... $d\underline{x}$

function of x .... $f(\underline{x})$

integral of y with respect to x .... $\int \underline{y}\, d\underline{x}$

integral of y from $x = a$ to $x = b$ .... $\int_{\underline{a}}^{\underline{b}} \underline{y}\, d\underline{x}$

vector of magnitude A .... $\underset{\sim}{A}$

scalar product of A and B .... $\underset{\sim}{A} \cdot \underset{\sim}{B}$

vector product of A and B .... $\underset{\sim}{A} \times \underset{\sim}{B},\ \underset{\sim\sim}{AB}$

matrix A .... $\underset{\sim}{A}$

ABBREVIATIONS, SYMBOLS, AND UNITS

The use of abbreviations and symbols is recommended wherever space is limited, as in lists, tables, illustrations, and experimental sections as well as in equations. In titles, abstracts, and text material, however, abbreviations should be used sparingly.

Symbols for chemical compounds and physical quantities should follow the recommendations of the American Chemical Society and those of the commissions of the International Union of Pure and Applied Chemistry or International Union of Biochemistry (see pp 38-44 and Nomenclature References pp 50-54).

A specialized abbreviation may be used provided:
1. it is not an abbreviation of weight or measure;
2. it does not involve a drug with a generic name;
3. there is no standard abbreviation already in existence;
4. it will not be confused with the symbol of an element;
5. the term is defined in a footnote, the text, or a nomenclature list included at the end of the paper.

Abbreviations for specialized terms which appear frequently in a paper should be given in parentheses following the full name when it appears for the first time. Thereafter the abbreviation may be used alone.*

Symbols should be used in the text in such a way that their translation

---

*In *Biochemistry* all abbreviations for the paper should be identified in a footnote to the first abbreviation.

into words or phrases will require no effort on the part of the reader. Their meanings must always be unambiguous. Indiscriminate use of symbols may lead to cryptic writing, and authors should consider carefully the questions of style that arise from this practice.

Special attention must be given to the following recommendations on general principles concerning the use of symbols and abbreviations.

(1) A clear distinction is to be drawn between a) *symbols for physical quantities* and b) *other symbols and abbreviations* including those denoting mathematical operations and constants, symbols for the chemical elements, and abbreviations for words and for the names of units.

Symbols for physical quantities are always printed in italic type. These symbols normally consist of single letters of the Latin or the Greek alphabet with or without subscripts, superscripts, or other modifying signs. Where letters of the Latin alphabet (capitals or lower case) are used as subscripts, they are also to be printed in *italic* type if the subscript itself represents a physical quantity. In other cases the subscript shall be in Roman (upright) type.

e.g., C_g C_p , typewritten as $\underline{C}_g$ $\underline{C}_p$

Boldface type should be used for *vector quantities* (see also pp 35, 38).

e.g., *A, a* **S, T** , typewritten as $\underset{\sim}{\underline{A}}, \underset{\sim}{\underline{a}}$ $\underset{\sim}{S}, \underset{\sim}{T}$

Where letters of the Latin alphabet are used for other symbols and abbreviations for any of the purposes listed in *b* above, they are to be printed in Roman type.

(2) Chemical and mathematical copy should be precisely and carefully arranged. Haste and carelessness in the typing or drawing of symbols may lead to excessive cost in later stages of publishing through misinterpretation of the author's intent.

Letter symbols representing variables in mathematical expressions should be underlined for italics in the manuscript to avoid confusion with abbreviations or symbols for the chemical elements which are to be set in Roman type.

Symbols which may be difficult to interpret are best explained in marginal pencil notes. Special attention should be given to Greek letters. Note that the capital Greek letters A, B, E, Z, H, I, K, M, N, O, P, T, and X are like certain English letters and may not be suitable as symbols. Greek letters that appear in a manuscript should not be underlined by the author.

Symbols are spaced just as the words that they represent would be spaced if written in ordinary language structure. Lack of spacing before and after symbols makes for delayed and confused reading just as would wordswithoutspacing. Exceptions are parentheses, brackets, braces, plus quantities or minus quantities, and superscripts and subscripts. For example:

$$\underline{a} + \underline{b} = \underline{c} \qquad \text{not} \qquad \underline{a} + \underline{b} = \underline{c}$$

$$-\underline{x} + \underline{y} = \underline{z} \qquad \text{not} \qquad -\underline{x} + \underline{y} = \underline{z}$$

$$e^{-(\underline{k}+1)(\underline{x}-\underline{t})} \qquad \text{not} \qquad e^{-(\underline{k}+1)(\underline{x}-\underline{t})}$$

(3) Where it is necessary to select from alternative symbols for a quantity, or to adopt symbols for quantities for which there are no widely accepted specific symbols, consideration should be given to current practice by authorities in the field and to the desirability of adopting a single set of self-consistent symbols. The author then must define clearly in his paper all terms and units. The selected symbols should be such as to permit modification in accordance with a uniform scheme for the representation of any important series of corresponding derived quantities.

(4) Symbols (or abbreviations) representing the names of units are used following or preceding a number.

For example, "The area of the auxiliary electrode was 1.0 cm^2." but, "Mercury was added to a depth of a few millimeters."

Authors are urged to use the recommended units of measurements and symbols and prefixes (see pp 45-49).

(5) The same abbreviation and symbol is applicable to either the singular or the plural form of the word.

(6) *Most abbreviations are used without periods* except when they appear at the end of a sentence. Periods should always be omitted after symbols representing the names of units and physical quantities except where this cannot be done without causing ambiguity.

It is customary, however, to use a period after initials in the name of a person, and after abbreviations of Latin expressions (i.e., etc., cf.).

(7) Symbols and abbreviations denoting *mathematical operations and constants* should follow the standard practice of mathematicians.

(8) There are no rigid rules for the use of *modifying signs* such as subscripts, superscripts, and brackets, but a satisfactory notation should:
a) be unambiguous.
b) be systematic, simple, and easy to remember.
c) not use more letters and characters than necessary.
For example, where a subscript has to be added to a symbol which already carries a subscript, the two subscripts should be separated by a comma.

i.e., $a_{Na,R}$

In thermochemical work, such an equation as

$$Ag(s) + H^+(aq) + Cl^-(aq) = AgCl(s) + 1/2H_2(g)$$

is preferable with full-size letters and parentheses. The form

$$Ag_{(s)} + H^+_{(aq)} + Cl^-_{(aq)} = AgCl_{(s)} + 1/2H_2(g)$$

requires expensive hand-filling of the parenthesized subscripts.

(9) Brackets, including parentheses ( ), braces { }, and square brackets [ ], should not be used around the symbol for a quantity to make it represent any other quantity, unless such use is consistently adopted for an entire class of quantities as in crystallography. Square brackets [ ] enclosing a formula of a chemical species to indicate its molar concentration fulfills the above general requirements.

In crystallography it is recommended that:

Miller indices be enclosed in parentheses, ( );

Laue indices be unenclosed;

indices of a form be enclosed in braces, { } ;

indices of a zone axis or line be enclosed in square brackets, [ ].

Most other uses of brackets, apart from their mathematical uses, should be avoided.

SPECIFIC USAGES
International communication in science continues to grow in importance. The International Union of Pure and Applied Chemistry (IUPAC) and the International Union of Biochemistry (IUB) are concerned with academic and industrial aspects of chemistry for which international agreement and uniform practice is desirable. Examples are nomenclature, atomic weights, symbols and terminology, physicochemical constants, methods of analysis and assay. IUPAC and IUB, through their Divisions, Sections, and Commissions, serve as international forums where the views of outstanding specialists in many fields of chemical interest are presented, discussed, and, after approval, published. (See pp 50-54 for a list of references including IUPAC and IUB documents.) The U. S. is represented in IUPAC and IUB by the Division of Chemistry and Chemical Technology of the National Academy of Sciences—National Research Council. An Office of Biochemical Nomenclature cosponsored by several Divisions of the National Research Council was recently established. Its principal objectives are to receive and to supply information about all activities in the field of biochemical nomenclature in the U. S. and abroad, to aid in the distribution of rules agreed upon at the international level, and to collect any criticisms about these rules for transmission to the IUPAC-IUB Commission. The American Chemical Society through its Committee on Nomenclature (see p 49) also contributes to the IUPAC and IUB work.

The preferred usages for symbols and abbreviations for the Society's journals are presented on the following pages. These examples are based on IUPAC and IUB recommendations.

SYMBOLS FOR PHYSICAL AND CHEMICAL QUANTITIES
Symbols for physical and chemical quantities should be printed in *italic* type; therefore they must be underlined in the manuscript.

Subscripts or superscripts which are themselves symbols for physical quantities should be italicized; all others should be in Roman type,

e.g., C_p, typewritten as $\underline{C}_p$, for heat capacity at constant pressure,

but C_B, typewritten as $\underline{C}_B$, for heat capacity of substance B.

Vectors should be printed in bold italic type, *e.g., A, a*, typewritten as

$\underset{\sim}{\underline{A}}$, $\underset{\sim}{\underline{a}}$, and *tensors* of the second rank should be printed in bold

Roman type *e.g.,* **S, T**, typewritten as $\underset{\sim}{S}$, $\underset{\sim}{T}$.

A list of commonly used symbols follows:*
(Symbols separated by commas represent equivalent recommendations. Symbols preceded by three dots are alternatives to be used only when there is some reason for not using a symbol before the three dots.)

---

*Reprinted from the *Journal of the American Chemical Society*, **82**, 5519 (1960); 1958 Report of the IUPAC Commission on Physico-chemical Symbols and Terminology. This list is now being revised by the IUPAC Commission.

Space, time, mass, and related quantities

1 length l
2 height h
3 radius r
4 diameter d
5 path, length of arc s
6 plane angle $\alpha, \beta, \gamma, \theta, \phi, \psi$
7 solid angle ω
8 area A, S
9 volume $V...v$
10 specific volume v
11 wavelength λ
12 wavenumber σ, v
13 time t
14 period or other characteristic interval T, τ
15 frequency v, f
16 angular frequency $(2\pi v)$ ω
17 velocity $v...u, w$
18 angular velocity ω
19 acceleration a
20 acceleration of free fall g
21 mass m
22 moment of inertia I
23 density ρ
24 relative density d

Molecular and related quantities

101 molecular mass m
102 molar mass M
103 Avogadro's number N_0, L, N
104 number of molecules N
105 number of moles n
106 mole fraction $x...X, y$
107 molality m
108 concentration c
109 molar concentration of substance B c_B, [B], $c(B)$
110 molecular concentration C
111 partition function Q
112 statistical weight $g...p$
113 symmetry number σ
114 characteristic temperature Θ
115 diameter of molecule $\sigma...D$
116 mean free path l
117 diffusion coefficient D
118 osmotic pressure Π
119 surface concentration Γ

Mechanical and related quantities

201 force F
202 force due to gravity (weight) $G...W$
203 moment of force M
204 power P
205 pressure p, P
206 traction σ
207 shear stress τ
208 modulus of elasticity E
209 shear modulus G
210 compressibility κ
211 compression modulus $(1/\kappa)$ K
212 viscosity η
213 fluidity ϕ
214 kinematic viscosity v
215 friction coefficient f
216 surface tension $\gamma...\sigma$
217 angle of contact θ

Thermodynamic and related quantities

301 temperature $\theta...t$
302 temperature, absolute T
303 gas constant $R, \boldsymbol{R}$
304 Boltzmann constant $k, \boldsymbol{k}$
305 heat q, Q
306 work w, A

	a	b
307 energy (Gibbs ϵ)	$U...E$	$E...U$
308 entropy (Gibbs η)	S	S
*309 Helmholtz free energy (Gibbs ψ)	F	A
310 enthalpy (Gibbs χ)	H	H
*311 Gibbs function (ζ)	G	$G...F$

a Recommended by IUPAP (without...E), European practice.

b American practice.

312 heat capacity C
313 specific heats c_p, c_v
314 ratio c_p/c_v γ, κ
315 chemical potential μ
316 activity, absolute λ
317 activity, relative a
318 activity coefficient f, γ
319 osmotic coefficient g, ϕ
320 thermal conductivity λ
321 Joule-Thomson coefficient μ

Chemical reactions

401 stoichiometric number of molecules (negative for reactants, positive for products) v
402 standard equation of chemical reaction $\Sigma v_{B}B = 0$
403 affinity ($-\Sigma v_{B}\mu_{B}$) of a reaction A
404 equilibrium constant K
405 equilibrium quotient or equilibrium product (of molalities) Q
406 extent of reaction ($dn_{B} = v_{B}d\xi$) ξ
407 degree of reaction (*e.g.*, degree of dissociation) α
408 rate constant k
409 collision number (collisions per unit volume and unit time) Z
410 rate constant corresponding to the rate Z z
411 rate of reaction $v...r, s, J$

Light

501 Planck's constant $h, \boldsymbol{h}$
502 Planck's constant divided by 2π $\hbar$
503 quantity of light Q
504 radiant power, flux of light (dQ/dt) Φ
505 luminous intensity ($d\Phi/d\omega$) I
506 illumination ($d\Phi/dS$) E
507 luminance L, B
508 luminous emittance H
509 absorption factor (fraction of incident radiant power which is absorbed) α
510 reflection factor (fraction of incident radiant power which is reflected) ρ
511 transmission factor (fraction of incident radiant power which is transmitted) τ
512 transmittance ($T = I/I_0$) T
513 absorption (extinction) coefficient ($\kappa lc = \ln (1/T)$) κ
514 absorbance (extinction) ($A = \log (1/T)$) $A...E$
515 absorptivity (specific absorbance) (decadic absorption or extinction coefficient) a
516 molar absorptivity (molar decadic absorption or extinction coefficient) ($\epsilon lc = A$) ϵ
517 refraction index n
518 refractivity r
519 angle of optical rotation α

---

*The terms for the Helmholtz and Gibbs energies were modified by action of the IUPAC Council—see *Comptes Rendus de la Vingt et Unième Conférence*, Montreal, 2-5 August, 1961, Butterworths Scientific Publications, London, Minute 25, p 122.

The approved symbols for items 309 and 311 above are now as follows:
309 Helmholtz Energy (Gibbs $\psi = E - TS$) A
311 Gibbs Energy (Gibbs $\zeta = H - TS$) G

Electricity and magnetism

601 elementary charge $e, \boldsymbol{e}$
602 quantity of electricity Q
603 charge density ρ
604 surface charge density σ
605 electric current $I...i$
606 electric current density J
607 electric potential V
608 electric field strength E
609 electric displacement D
610 electrokinetic potential ζ
611 capacity C
612 permittivity (dielectric constant) ϵ
613 dielectric polarization P
614 dipole moment μ
615 electric polarizability of a molecule α, γ
616 magnetic field strength H
617 magnetic induction B
618 magnetic permeability μ
619 magnetization M
620 magnetic susceptibility χ
621 resistance R
622 resistivity ρ
623 self inductance L
624 mutual inductance M, L_{12}
625 reactance X
626 impedance Z
627 admittance Y

Electrochemistry

701 Faraday's constant (the faraday) $F, \boldsymbol{F}$
702 charge number of an ion, plus or minus z
703 degree of electrolytic dissociation α
704 ionic strength $I...\mu$
705 electrolytic conductivity (specific conductance) κ
706 equivalent or molar conductance of electrolyte or ion Λ
707 transport number t, T
708 electromotive force E
709 overpotential η

SYMBOLS FOR CHEMICAL ELEMENTS, NUCLIDES, AND PARTICLES

Symbols for chemical elements should be written in Roman type. The symbol is not followed by a period.

e.g., Ca, C, H, He

In accordance with IUPAC recommendation, "the mass number, atomic number, number of atoms, and ionic charge of an element may be indicated by means of four indices placed around the symbol. The positions are to be occupied thus: left upper index, mass number; left lower index, atomic number; right upper index, ionic charge, right lower index, number of atoms."

e.g., $^{12}_{6}C$ Ca^{2+}

The atomic number which is redundant may be omitted in most cases,

i.e., ^{12}C

Ionic charge should be indicated by a superscript plus or minus sign following the symbol of the ion; for multiple charges an Arabic superscript numeral should *precede* the plus or minus sign.

e.g., Na^+, NO_3^-, Ca^{2+}, PO_4^{3-}, $^{7}Li^-$

41

The oxidation state of an element is indicated by a Roman numeral on the line and in parentheses.

e.g., cobalt(III)   or   Co(III)

If necessary the oxidation state of an element in *a formula of a compound* may be indicated by a superscript Roman numeral without parentheses following the symbol of the element.

In the formula of a free radical the unshared electron may be indicated by a point in the middle position.

e.g., $H_3C\cdot$, $C_6H_5\cdot$, $HO\cdot$

A centered period is also used for water of hydration in chemical formulas.

e.g., $Na_2SO_4 \cdot 10H_2O$

The mass number of an isotope should be used as a superior prefix only to the atomic symbol, not to an abbreviation:

$[^{32}P]CMP$ not $CM^{32}P$ $[^{14}C]urea$

$[\alpha\text{-}^{14}C]leucine$ $\underline{\underline{L}}\text{-}[\underline{methyl}\text{-}^{14}C]methionine$

Symbols for particles and quanta are as follows:

neutron	n	pion	π
proton	p	muon	μ
deuteron	d	electron	e
triton	t	neutrino	ν
α-particle	α	photon	γ

The meaning of abbreviated notations for nuclear reactions should be the following:

$$\text{initial nuclide} \left(\begin{matrix} \text{incoming} & \text{outgoing} \\ \text{particle(s)} & \text{particle(s)} \\ \text{or quanta,} & \text{or quanta} \end{matrix} \right) \text{final nuclide}$$

Examples:

$^{14}N(\alpha, p)^{17}O$ $^{59}Co(n, \gamma)^{60}Co$

$^{23}Na(\gamma, 3n)^{20}Na$ $^{31}P(\gamma, pn)^{29}Si$

SYMBOLS AND ABBREVIATIONS FOR CHEMICAL AND BIOCHEMICAL COMPOUNDS

The limited use of abbreviations and symbols of specified meaning for the names of chemical substances is accepted, especially in instances which would otherwise require the repeated use of unwieldy terms. However, clarity and unambiguity are more important than brevity.

Compounds listed and described in a paper may be numbered by bold-face Arabic numerals. When referring to numbered compounds parentheses are used when the compound number is not really necessary but simply aids in identification; parentheses are not used where the number is essential.

e.g. Four grams of 11β-hydroxyprogesterone (4) was dissolved...

Compound 2 was treated with...

The oxidation product contained a keto alcohol, 3, which...

Nonstandard abbreviations and symbols when used in a paper should not conflict with known ones, or with the general principles proposed in the nomenclature rules. Nonstandard abbreviations should *always* be defined in each paper.

As many of the recommendations for abbreviations presented in the nomenclature reports on the various areas of chemistry should be followed as is possible in the light of individual circumstances (see Nomenclature References pp 50-54). A few of these recommendations have been selected and are presented in the following list.

(1) The prefixes *cis, trans, sym, asym* should be connected with the chemical formula by a hyphen and they should be italicized.

e.g., cis-[PtCl$_2$ (NH$_3$)$_2$]

(2) The *stoichiometric proportions* may be denoted by means of prefixes, such as mono, di, tri, bis, tris, preceding without hyphen the names of the elements or groups to which they refer. These prefixes are not italicized.

e.g., N$_2$S$_5$ dinitrogen pentasulfide

[Co(H$_2$ NCH$_2$ CH$_2$ NH$_2$)$_3$]Cl$_3$

tris(ethylenediamine)cobalt(III) chloride

(3) The proportions of the constituents in a formula also may be indicated indirectly by *Stock's System,* that is, by Roman numerals representing the oxidation state of the element, placed in parentheses immediately following the name. For zero the Arabic 0 should be used. When used in conjunction with symbols the Roman numeral may be placed above and to the right. The Stock notation can be applied to both cations and anions.

e.g., FeCl$_2$ iron(II) chloride

MnO$_2$ manganese(IV) oxide

K$_4$[Ni(CN)$_4$]   potassium tetracyanonickelate(0)

[Cr(H$_2$O)$_6$](ClO$_4$)$_3$

hexaaquochromium (III) perchlorate

(4) In di- and polynuclear compounds a bridging group should be indicated by adding the Greek letter μ immediately before its name and separating this from the rest of the complex by a hyphen. Two or more bridging groups of the same kind are indicated by di-μ-, etc.

e.g., Be$_4$O(CH$_3$COO)$_6$

μ_4-oxo-hexa-μ-acetato-tetraberyllium

(5) For chemical purposes polymorphs should be indicated by adding the crystal system after the name or formula.

e.g., ZnS (cub) = zinc blende or sphalerite

ZnS (hex) = wurtzite

The following abbreviations proposed by IUPAC should be considered: *

| cub | cubic | f | face-centered |
| c | body-centered | tetr | tetragonal |

*Reprinted from the *Journal of the American Chemical Society,* **82,** 5544 (1960); 1957 Report of the IUPAC Commission on Nomenclature of Inorganic Chemistry.

o-rh	orthorhombic	mon	monoclinic
hex	hexagonal	tric	triclinic
trig	trigonal		

(6) In general, *configurational relationships* should be denoted by capital italic Roman letter prefixes R and S. The RS system is based on the actual three-dimensional formula of the compound to be named (see reference 14 on page 52).

In carbohydrate and amino acid nomenclature configurational relationships are usually denoted by the small capital Roman letter prefixes D and L.

The *optical rotational sign* under specified conditions is indicated by $(+)$ or $(-)$. *Racemic modifications* may be indicated by the prefixes DL or $(\pm)$. Where applicable the prefix *meso-* is employed.

e.g., D-Glucose   or   D-(+)-glucose

D-Fructose   or   D-(-)-fructose

(7) Certain specialized symbols and abbreviations are permitted without definition in several of the journals. Specific recommendations for specialized nomenclature may be found in the *Notice to or Guide for Authors* published in each journal.

Special symbols, although they may be fairly common, should be defined in any paper if it is thought that readers might be unfamiliar with them.

ABBREVIATIONS FOR WORDS OTHER THAN NAMES OF UNITS

The words in this list may appear often in full in the text of a manuscript, but where abbreviations are used the following forms are recommended.

absolute	abs
alternating current (adj)	ac
anhydrous	anhyd
approximate	*ca.*
aqueous	aq
atomic weight	at. wt
average	av
biological, biologically	biol
boiling point	bp
calculated	calcd
chemically pure	CP
circa (about)	*ca.*
circular dichroism	CD
coefficient	coeff
compound	compd
concentrated	concd
concentration	concn
confer (compare)	*cf.*
constant	const
corrected	cor
critical	crit
crystalline	cryst
current density	cd
decompose	dec
diameter	diam
differential thermoanalysis	dta
dilute	dil
direct current (adj)	dc
distilled	dist
dropping mercury electrode	dme
edited, edition	ed

editor	Ed.
effective dose—fifty	ED_{50}
electromotive force	emf
electron spin resonance	esr
equation	eq
equivalent weight	equiv wt
et alii (and others)	*et al.*
et cetera	etc.
exempli gratia (for example)	*e.g.*
experiment	expt
experimental	exptl
freezing point	fp
gas	(g), as in $H_2O(g)$
gas liquid partition chromatography	glpc
Ibidem (in the same place)	*ibid.*
id est (that is)	*i.e.*
infective dose—fifty	ID_{50}
infrared	ir
inside diameter	i.d.
insoluble	insol
lethal dose—fifty	LD_{50}
liquid	(l), as in $H_2O(l)$
maximum	max
melting point	mp
minimum	min
mixture melting point (not mixed melting point)	mmp
molecular weight	mol wt
mole per cent	mol %
neutralization equivalent	neut equiv

nuclear magnetic resonance	nmr	specific gravity	sp gr
observed	obsd	specific heat	sp ht
outside diameter	o.d.	specific volume	sp vol
page(s)	p (pp)	standard	std
parts per million	ppm	symmetrical	sym
parts per billion		temperature	temp
(parts per 10^9)	ppb	thermogravimetric analysis	tga
per cent	%	thin-layer chromatography	tlc
potential difference	pd	ultraviolet	uv
precipitate	ppt	United States Pharmacopoeia	USP
preparation	prepn	vacuum	vac
recrystallized	recryst	vapor pressure	vp
reference(s)	ref	versus	vs.
saturated calomel electrode	sce	volume	vol
solid	(s), as in AgCl(s)	volume per cent	vol %
soluble	sol	volume per volume	v/v
solution	soln	weight	wt
specific	sp	weight per cent	wt %

SYSTEMS OF UNITS   Scientists and engineers use only two major systems of units, usually called "British" and "Metric," but within each system many different units are in use for the same quantities. There is no uniformity as to the choice of, for example, the hour or the second and the foot or the inch. This problem of units adds quite substantially to the difficulty of the subject.

The *British System* of measurement is many centuries old; the yard and the pound, with their multiples (*e.g.,* mile) and divisions (*e.g.,* ounce) are basic in this system.

The *Metric System,* founded in the eighteenth century, has been adopted for general use by most countries, the notable exceptions being the British Commonwealth (apart from India) and the United States, and nearly everywhere it is used for precise measurements in science. The meter and the kilogram, with their decimal multiples (*e.g.,* kilometer) and fractions (*e.g.,* gram) are basic in this system. Whereas, British units of the same kind are related almost at random, the metric system is exclusively *decimal.*

In the metric system, as in the British system, all but the simplest of measurements are made in terms of combinations of units. For example, grams per square meter or ounces per square yard. Such combinations of units are often called complex units.

In the metric system as used in chemistry, complex quantities are measured mainly in terms of three units—the centimeter, the gram, and the second—in the mass-length-time system of dimensions. This is called the *CGS System. Except for a few exceptions in reporting engineering data, authors of papers to American Chemical Society journals should use the CGS System.*

In problems involving units of mechanics and electromagnetic units the *MKSA or Giorgi System* is used. This system is based on the following quantities: the meter, the kilogram, the second, and the ampere.

Definitions of other specialized systems and units (*e.g.,* the franklin, the biot, the oersted, the gauss, used in the "electrostatic CGS" and "electromagnetic CGS" unit systems) can be found in the International Organization for Standardization (ISO) document "Quantities and Units of Electricity and Magnetism" or in the International Union of Pure and Applied Physics (IUPAP) document U.I.P. 11 (S.U.N. 65-3) "Symbols, Units and Nomenclature in Physics."

The *International System* of units was adopted by the eleventh General Conference on Weights and Measures in 1960 and was endorsed by the

International Organization for Standardization. It appears to have every prospect of being adopted throughout the world, and of eventually superseding all others, in every branch of science, engineering, and commerce. The International System units (SI) have been recommended by the national standardizing bodies in many countries.* The Editors of the American Chemical Society journals wish to draw attention to the SI system and hope that authors will use it increasingly in the future. Additional basic information about the International System for future reference is included in Appendix 2.

Engineering Conventions for Dimensions and Units. Many branches of the engineering profession throughout the world tend to use the force-length-time system of dimensions in contradistinction to the mass-length-time system of dimensions so widely used by the scientific community. The force-length-time system of dimensions forms a satisfactory means of describing natural phenomena and in that system the dimensions of length and time are defined in the same fashion as in the mass-length-time system. However, the unit of force in the force-length-time system of dimensions is conventionally defined as the force exerted by a unit of mass in the mass-length-time system under the action of standard gravity.

In addition there has evolved in the United States a hybrid system of dimensions using the four dimensions of force, mass, length, and time to describe natural phenomena together with a conversion factor for the units of mass to units of force. The use of this system with four dimensions has gained acceptance particularly in the chemical engineering profession and when not carefully applied leads to redundancies in the description of natural phenomena and sometimes to inaccuracies as well.

In publications primarily of engineering interest, such as *I&EC Fundamentals, I&EC Process Design and Development, I&EC Product Research and Development,* and the *Journal of Chemical and Engineering Data,* papers are accepted in which the phenomena are described in the force-length-time and the force-mass-length-time systems of dimensions as well as in the mass-length-time system. However, authors are urged to be consistent throughout a given manuscript; only a single system of dimensions should be employed in any one contribution.

The following references are also informative:

1. Pamela Anderton and P. H. Bigg, "Changing to the Metric System. Conversion Factors, Symbols and Definitions," Her Majesty's Stationery Office, London, 1965.
2. E. A. Mechtly, "The International System of Units. Physical Constants and Conversion Factors," National Aeronautics and Space Administration SP-7012 (1964).
3. C. H. Page, "IEEE Recommended Practice for Units in Published Scientific and Technical Work," *IEEE (Inst. Elec. Electron. Eng.) Spectrum,* **3**, 169 (1966).
4. F. B. Silsbee, "Systems of Electrical Units," National Bureau of Standards Monograph 56, Washington, D. C., 1962.

*In the United States the National Bureau of Standards has announced in its Administrative Bulletin, 64-6 (February 1964) that:
"Henceforth it shall be the policy of the National Bureau of Standards to use the units of the International System (SI), as adopted by the 11th General Conference on Weights and Measures . . . , except when the use of these units would obviously impair communications or reduce the usefulness of a report to the primary recipients."

5. F. B. Silsbee, "Extension and Dissemination of the Electrical and Magnetic Units," National Bureau of Standards Circular 531, Washington, D. C., 1962.

6. International Organization for Standardization: ISO Recommendation R-31, Quantities, Units, Symbols, Conversion Factors and Conversion Tables. Copies may be obtained through the respective national standards organizations: in the U. S., American Standards Association Inc., 10 E. 40th St., New York, N. Y. 10016.

PART I: 1956, 1st edition, Fundamental Quantities and Units of the MKSA System and Units of Space and Time.
2nd edition, title changed to International System of Units and Quantities and Units of Space and Time (approved by ISO Council in 1965).

PART II: 1958, 1st edition, Quantities and Units of Periodic and Related Phenomena.

PART III: 1960, 1st edition, Quantities and Units of Mechanics.

PART IV: 1960, 1st edition, Quantities and Units of Heat.

PART V: 1965, 1st edition, Quantities and Units of Electricity and Magnetism (approved by ISO Council in 1965).

PART VII: 1965, 1st edition, Quantities and Units of Acoustics (approved by ISO Council in 1965).

PART XI: 1961, 1st edition, Mathematical Signs and Symbols for Use in the Physical Sciences and Technology.

UNITS AND THEIR SYMBOLS The following usages are recommended for the writing and printing of symbols for units:

(1) The symbol for a unit is printed in Roman type. It should remain unaltered in the plural, and except when it occurs at the end of a sentence in text, usually should not be followed by a period.

e.g., 2 cm not 2 cm. nor 2 cms. nor 2 cms

(2) The following prefixes may be combined with the basic unit symbols:

d	deci ($= 10^{-1}$)	p	pico ($= 10^{-12}$)
c	centi ($= 10^{-2}$)	k	kilo ($= 10^{3}$)
m	milli ($= 10^{-3}$)	M	mega ($= 10^{6}$)
μ	micro ($= 10^{-6}$)	G	giga ($= 10^{9}$)
n	nano ($= 10^{-9}$)	T	tera ($= 10^{12}$)

(3) Symbols for prefixes for units are also printed in Roman type with no space between the prefix and the unit. The use of double prefixes should be avoided when single prefixes are available.

e.g., nsec (nanosecond) *not* mμsec for 10^{-9} sec

(4) The combination of prefix and symbol should be considered as a single symbol which may be raised to a power without the use of parentheses.

e.g., cm², μA²

(5) The recommendations for representation of multiplication or division of units parallel those for products and quotients of quantity symbols (see pp 33, 34).

(6) More than one solidus (/) should never be used in the same expression unless parentheses are used to eliminate ambiguity.

e.g., cal $°K^{-1}$ mol^{-1} or cal/($°K$ mol) but *not* cal/$°K$/mol

l. mol^{-1} sec^{-1} or l. /(mol sec)

(l. /mol/sec, which is sometimes encountered, means

l. sec mol^{-1} and should not be used.)

(7) Units of measurement should be abbreviated when used with numerals but they are usually written out when they occur in the text without numerals. The following list of abbreviations is not exhaustive; it represents units and symbols most often encountered. Discrepancies between American Chemical Society and international usages are few and are gradually decreasing. Several British system units are included; their use is restricted to a few engineering papers. Metric units are preferred and recommended.

Unit	Abbreviation used in American Chemical Society journals	Common international usage
ampere	A	A
ängström	Å	Å
atmosphere	atm	atm
(unified) atomic mass unit	amu	u
bar	bar	bar
British thermal unit	Btu	Btu
Bohr Magneton	BM, μB	μB
calorie, thermochemical	cal	cal
centimeter	cm	cm
centipoise	cP	cP
coulomb	C	C
counts per minute	cpm	—
cubic centimeter	cm³	cm³
cubic foot	ft³	ft³
cubic meter	m³	m³
cycles per second	Hz, cps	Hz
Curie	Ci	Ci
Debye unit	D	—
degree Celsius (Centigrade)	—°	°C
degree Fahrenheit	°F	°F
degree Kelvin	°K	°K
disintegrations per minute	dpm	—
dyne	dyn	dyn
electromagnetic unit	emu	emu
electronvolt	eV	eV
electrostatic unit	esu	esu
erg	erg	erg
farad	F	F
foot	ft	ft
gauss	G	G
gram	g	g
gram atom	g-atom	—
henry	H	H
hertz	Hz	Hz
hour	hr	h
inch	in.	in
joule	J	J
kilocalorie	kcal	kcal
kilocycles per second	kcps, kHz	kHz
kilogram	kg	kg
liter	l.	l
lumen	lm	lm
lux	lx	lx

maxwell	Mx	Mx
megacycles per second	Mcps, MHz	MHz
meter	m	m
microampere	μA	μA
microbar	μbar	μbar
microliter	μl	μl
micron	μ	μm (micrometer)
milliampere	mA	mA
milligram	mg	mg
milliliter	ml	ml
millimeter	mm	mm
millimicron	mμ	mμ
million electron volts	MeV	MeV
minute	min	min
mole	mol	mol
molal (concentration)	m	m
molar (concentration)	M (M in *Biochemistry*)	M
Newton	N	N
normal (concentration)	N (N in *Biochemistry*)	N
oersted	Oe	Oe
ohm	ohm, Ω	Ω
ounce	oz	oz
pH (measure of hydrogen ion activity)	pH	pH
pK ($-\log K$)	pK	pK
pound	lb	lb
poise	P	P
radian	radian	rad
revolutions per minute	rpm	rpm
Roentgen	R	R
second	sec	s
square centimeter	cm^2	cm^2
square meter	m^2	m^2
steradian	sr	sr
Stokes	St	St
volt	V	V
watt	W	W

NOMENCLATURE

All nomenclature should be consistent and unambiguous. The chemical names for drugs should be used. In cases where the terminology is unwieldy, the generic names, if available, may be used throughout the manuscript after the first mention. Formally adopted generic names are listed in *United States Adopted Names* (USAN).

Trade names should be avoided whenever possible. They should not be used in the title or in abstracts of articles. Trade names, if they must be used, should always be capitalized.

Code numbers referring to original laboratory records should not be used to identify compounds.

The ACS Committee on Nomenclature,* whose objective is the development and promotion of good nomenclature in all chemical fields, cooperates with other groups such as the Nomenclature Commissions of the International Union of Pure and Applied Chemistry, the National Academy of Sciences-National Research Council Office of Biochemical Nomenclature, and the ACS divisional committees. Authors should consider seriously the recommendations and reports of these groups.

*The present Chairman is Dr. Kurt L. Loening, Chemical Abstracts Service, The Ohio State University, Columbus, Ohio 43210.

The Chemical Abstracts Service (CAS) continues to be the Society's headquarters for the distribution of nomenclature pamphlets and other nomenclature information. See p 53 for a list of pamphlets available from CAS. As guides to acceptable nomenclature the subject indexes to *Chemical Abstracts,* especially the Introduction to Volume 56, should be consulted. *"The Naming and Indexing of Chemical Compounds from Chemical Abstracts,"* a revised and much expanded version of the 1957 edition, is in preparation. It should be recognized that *Chemical Abstracts* rules are designed to furnish a single unambiguous name for any compound primarily for indexing purposes. This name may not be suitable or even desirable for use in text.

The following references are recommended:

1. *Manual of Physico-Chemical Symbols and Terminology.*
   (IUPAC Physical Chemistry Section, Commission of Physico-Chemical Symbols and Terminology, 1958).
   J. Amer. Chem. Soc., **82,** 5517 (1960).

2. *Nomenclature of Inorganic Chemistry.*
   (1957 Report of the IUPAC Commission on the Nomenclature of Inorganic Chemistry).
   J. Amer. Chem. Soc., **82,** 5523 (1960).

3. *Definitive Rules for Nomenclature of Organic Chemistry.*
   (Report of the IUPAC Commission on the Nomenclature of Organic Chemistry, 1957). *Section A* (Hydrocarbons), *Section B* (Fundamental Heterocyclic Systems).
   J. Amer. Chem. Soc., **82,** 5545 (1960).
   Sections A and B plus *Definitive Rules for Nomenclature of Steroids* are also published in one volume by Butterworths Scientific Publications, London (1966).

4. *Definitive Rules for Nomenclature of Organic Chemistry. Section C* (Characteristic Groups Containing C, H, O, N, Halogen, S, Se and/or Te).
   Butterworths Scientific Publications, London (1965).
   Pure Appl. Chem., **11,** No. 1-2 (1965).

5. *Report on Nomenclature in the Field of Macromolecules.* (IUPAC Commission on Macromolecules, Subcommission on Nomenclature, 1951).
   J. Polym. Sci., **8,** 257 (1952); **56,** 153 (1962).

6. *Rules of Carbohydrate Nomenclature.*
   a. (Committee on Carbohydrate Nomenclature of IUPAC) Supplement to IUPAC Information Bulletin No. 17, 1962. Currently being revised.
   b. (Nomenclature Committee of the Division of Carbohydrate Chemistry of the American Chemical Society, and Subcommittee on Carbohydrate Nomenclature of the Publications Committee of The Chemical Society, London—the so-called "Anglo-American Rules," accepted by the Council of the American Chemical Society in 1962).
   J. Org. Chem., **28,** 281 (1963).

7. *Nomenclature of Organophosphorus Compounds.*
   (1952 rules agreed to between committees of The Chemical Society, London, and the American Chemical Society).
   "Handbook for Chemical Society Authors," The Chemical Society, London, 1960, p 155.
   Note: This source also contains items 1, 2, 3, 6b, and 8b.

8. *Definitive Rules for the Nomenclature of Amino Acids, Steroids, Vitamins, and Carotenoids.*

(IUPAC Commission on the Nomenclature of Biological Chemistry).

a. Amino Acids

J. Amer. Chem. Soc., **82**, 5575 (1960) (Rules AA1-10).

J. Org. Chem., **28**, 291 (1963) (Rule AA11).

See also item 9 and *J. Biol. Chem.*, **241**, 2491 (1966) for abbreviations and symbols.

b. Steroids

J. Amer. Chem. Soc., **82**, 5577 (1960).

IUPAC Information Bulletin No. 11, appendix B (the so-called "Basel" proposals).

c. Vitamins (now replaced)

J. Amer. Chem. Soc., **82**, 5581 (1960).

Note: Replaced by the following documents of the IUPAC-IUB combined Commission on Biochemical Nomenclature (CBN).

1. "Trivial Names of Miscellaneous Compounds of Importance in Biochemistry"

Biochim. Biophys. Acta, **107**, 1 (1965).

J. Biol. Chem., **241**, 2987 (1966).

2. "Nomenclature of Quinones with Isoprenoid Side Chains"

Biochim. Biophys. Acta, **107**, 5 (1965).

J. Biol. Chem., **241**, 2989 (1966).

3. "Nomenclature and Symbols for Folic Acid and Related Compounds"

Biochim. Biophys. Acta, **107**, 11 (1965).

J. Biol. Chem., **241**, 2991 (1966).

4. "Rules for the Nomenclature of Corrinoids"

Biochim. Biophys. Acta, **117**, 285 (1966).

J. Biol. Chem., **241**, 2991 (1966).

d. Carotenoids

J. Amer. Chem. Soc., **82**, 5583 (1960).

9. *Revised (1965) Tentative Rules for Abbreviations and Symbols for Chemical Names of Special Interest in Biological Chemistry.*

J. Biol. Chem., **241**, 527 (1966).

Biochemistry, **5**, 1445 (1966).

Section 5, on Nucleotides and Nucleic Acids, also appears in *Biochim. Biophys. Acta*, **108**, 1 (1965).

See also

Tentative Rules for the Abbreviated Designation of Amino Acid Derivatives and Peptides.

J. Biol. Chem., **241**, 2491 (1966).

Biochemistry, **5**, 2485 (1966).

Under Consideration by the IUPAC-IUB Commission on Biochemical Nomenclature

Nomenclature of Lipids

Semi-Trivial Names for Peptides

Nomenclature of Carbohydrates (see item 6a above), including Aminosugars

Nomenclature of Cyclitols

Representation of Biological Polymers

Carotenoid Nomenclature (to extend item 8d above)

Steroids (to extend item 8b above)

10. *Enzyme Nomenclature*

Report of the Commission on Enzymes of the International Union of Biochemistry.

International Union of Biochemistry (IUB) Symposium

Series No. 20, Pergamon Press, New York, N. Y., 1961.

Revised in 1964 (Elsevier, New York, N. Y., 1965).

11. *Proposal of Standard Conventions and Nomenclature for the Description of Polypeptide Conformations.*
    Biopolymers, **4**, 121 (1966).
    J. Biol. Chem., **241**, 1004 (1966).

12. *IUPAC Recommendations for Abbreviations of Terms Relating to Plastics and Elastomers.*
    IUPAC Information Bulletin No. 25, p 41, 1966.

13. *Nomenclature of Labeled Organic Molecules.*
    IUPAC Information Bulletin No. 20, p 27, 1964.

14. *Rules for Stereoisomers*
    "An Introduction to the Sequence Rule. A system for the specification of absolute configuration," R. S. Cahn, *J. Chem. Educ.,* **41**, 116 (1964).
    R. S. Cahn, C. K. Ingold, and V. Prelog, *Angew. Chem. Intern. Ed. Engl.,* **5**, 384 (1966).

15. A. M. Patterson, L. T. Capell, and D. F. Walker, "The Ring Index," 1960, and Supplements I, II, and III, American Chemical Society, Washington, D. C.

16. "Nomenclature Guidebook"
    A guide to organic nomenclature prepared by the ACS Division of Organic Chemistry. In press.

17. *Report on the Standardization of pH and Related Terminology.*
    Pure Appl. Chem., **1**, 163 (1960).

18. *Report of the International Commission on Atomic Weights.*
    J. Amer. Chem. Soc., **84**, 4175 (1962).

19. *Electrochemical Nomenclature and Definitions* (Report of CITCE)
    Commission of Electrochemical Nomenclature and Definitions and of the IUPAC Sub-Commission on Electrochemical Symbols and Terminology.
    Electrochim. Acta, **9**, 1343 (1964).
    J. Electroanal. Chem., **7**, 417 (1964).

20. *Electroanalytical Techniques.*
    Anal. Chem., **32**, 103A (1960).

21. *Revised Resolution on Data Publication,* 15th Calorimetry Conference.
    Science, **132**, 1658 (1960).

22. "Terminology and Symbols for Use in Ultraviolet, Visible, and Infrared Absorptometry."
    Letter Circular 857, National Bureau of Standards, Washington, D. C.

23. *Recommendations on Nomenclature and Presentation of Data in Gas Chromatography.*
    IUPAC Division of Analytical Chemistry.
    Pure Appl. Chem., **8**, No. 3-4, 553 (1964).

24. *Spectrometry.*
    Anal. Chem., **37**, 1814 (1965).

25. The following recommendations are under consideration by the IUPAC Division of Analytical Chemistry:
    IUPAC Information Bulletin No. 26, 1966.
    Symbols for Solution Equilibria, p 25
    Terminology of Liquid-Liquid Extraction, p 31
    Terminology for Automation, p 35
    Presentation of the Results of Chemical Analysis, p 39
    Nomenclature of Titrimetric Analysis, p 43
    Classification and Nomenclature of Electroanalytical Methods, p 55

The following nomenclature and related pamphlets are available at CAS and may be ordered from: Chemical Abstracts Service, Box 1378, Columbus, Ohio 43210. (All material is sent prepaid, parcel post. UNESCO coupons may be used.)

IUPAC Reports

Definitive Report of the IUPAC Commission on the Reform of the Nomenclature of Organic Chemistry. Report on the 1930 meeting at Liége. Translation with comment and index by Austin M. Patterson .... gratis

IUPAC Commission de nomenclature de chimie inorganique. Report on 1949 meeting at Amsterdam (in English). This relates to the names of new elements or others concerning which there has been controversy as to names .... gratis

IUPAC Commission de nomenclature de chimie organique. Report on 1949 meeting at Amsterdam (in English). This includes rules on the nomenclature of organosilicon compounds (now covered by "Organosilicon Compounds" below), changes and additions to the Definitive Report, extended examples of radical names, and an extensive list of radical names .... gratis

IUPAC 1957 Definitive Rules for Nomenclature of Organic Chemistry. Official report of the IUPAC Commission on Nomenclature of Organic Chemistry. This includes definitive rules for the nomenclature of acyclic and cyclic hydrocarbons and heterocyclic compounds, with comments $1.00

IUPAC Definitive Rules for the Nomenclature of Amino Acids, Steroids, Vitamins, and Carotenoids. Official report of the IUPAC Commission on Nomenclature of Biological Chemistry (1957) .... gratis

IUPAC 1957 Nomenclature of Inorganic Chemistry. Official report on the IUPAC Commission on Nomenclature of Inorganic Chemistry with comments by American Nomenclature Committees .... gratis

IUPAC Manual of Physico-Chemical Symbols and Terminology. Official report (with comments) of the IUPAC Commission on Physico-Chemical Symbols and Terminology (1959) .... gratis

Reports on Symbolism and Nomenclature. The above four reports bound together $3.00

ACS Committee Reports

The Pronunciation of Chemical Words (1934) .... gratis

Nomenclature of the Hydrogen Isotopes and Their Compounds (1935) .... gratis

The Nomenclature of the Carotenoid Pigments. Report (1946) of the Committee on Biochemical Nomenclature of the National Research Council accepted by the Committee on Nomenclature, Spelling, and Pronunciation of the American Chemical Society .... gratis

The Naming of Cis and Trans Isomers of Hydrocarbons Containing Olefin Double Bonds (1949) .... gratis

The Designation of "Extra" Hydrogen in Naming Cyclic Compounds (1949) .... gratis

The Naming of Geometric Isomers of Polyalkyl Monocycloalkanes (1950) .... gratis

Arene and Arylene (1952) ..... gratis

Halogenated Derivatives of Hydrocarbons (1952) .... gratis

Use of "Per" in Naming Halogenated Organic Compounds (1952) .... gratis

Use of "H" to Designate Position of Hydrogens in Almost Completely Fluorinated Organic Compounds (1952) .... gratis

Organic Compounds Containing Phosphorus (1952) .... gratis

Organosilicon Compounds (1952) gratis

Nomenclature of Natural Amino Acids and Related Substances (1952) .... gratis

Addendum to Nomenclature of Natural Amino Acids and Related Substances. Rule II.

Miscellaneous

For special rates on multiple copies for educational courses write to Chemical Abstracts Service.

In addition to the references listed above, the *Journal of Chemical Documentation* occasionally publishes articles dealing with nomenclature. These articles may or may not deal with nomenclature systems which have been officially reviewed and accepted by the American Chemical Society, hence the names recommended therein should not always be regarded as definitive or official.

PRESENTATION OF EXPERIMENTAL DETAILS

Use complete sentences in presenting data. The journal's style preferences concerning abbreviations, symbols, punctuation, and spacing should be closely followed.

(1) Data characterizing compounds should, in general, be presented as shown in the following example:

"The ethereal extract was dried ($MgSO_4$), concentrated, and distilled giving 10.23 g (65%) of the acetoxy ketone 12: bp 82-83° (2.9 mm); $n^{25}D$ 1.4266 [lit.[6] bp 80-82° (3 mm), $n^{25}D$ 1.4261]; d^{25}_4 0.823; $[\alpha]^{25}D$ 0.0 (c 6, CH_3OH); uv max (95% C_2H_5OH) 275 mμ (ε21.3); ir (CCl_4) 1725 (C=O) and 1740 cm^{-1} (ester C=O); nmr (CCl_4) δ3.98 (t, 2, J = 6 Hz,

$\underline{CH_2}OAc$), 2.43 (t, 2, $\underline{J}$ = 6 Hz, $\underline{CH_2}CO$), 2.07 (s, 3), 1.97 (s, 3), and 1.6 ppm (m, 4); mass spectrum (70 eV) $\underline{m/e}$ (rel intensity) 158 (5), 143 (5), 115 (6), 100 (50), 99 (11), 98 (100), 85 (10). "

In nmr descriptions, s = singlet, d = doublet, t = triplet, m = multiplet.

(2) Analytical results should be reported individually as shown below, or in tabular form. The order of elements is first carbon, then hydrogen, and the remaining elements in alphabetical order.

$\underline{Anal.}$ Calcd for $C_{10}H_{15}NO_7$:   C, 45.98; H, 5.79; N, 5.36.   Found: C, 46.02; H, 5.86: N, 5.35.

(3) Ultraviolet, infrared, magnetic resonance, or mass spectra will be reproduced only if this is essential to establish a conclusion or permit detailed interpretation. Otherwise, spectral data should be presented in numerical form in the experimental part, or, in exceptional cases, in tables. The same requirements apply to gas chromatographic data.

In preparing copy for reproduction of spectra, the general rules for illustrations apply (see p 65). Xerox or similar copies of spectra are seldom of adequate quality for use by the engraver. Only the pertinent part of a spectrum should be shown. The scale on the abscissa (and ordinate if pertinent) should be shown and should be consistent with units used in the paper. If structural formulas are included on spectra, drawing and

FIGURE 4.—Spectral data are reproduced only if this is essential to the author's presentation. In preparing copy for reproduction of spectra, the general rules for illustrations apply.

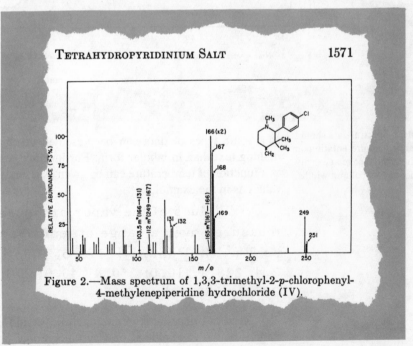

Figure 2.—Mass spectrum of 1,3,3-trimethyl-2-*p*-chlorophenyl-4-methylenepiperidine hydrochloride (IV).

lettering must be carefully done (see p 60). In bar graphs of mass spectra, *m/e* values of principal peaks should be lettered in on the graph; white space in such graphs can be advantageously used to denote fragmentation patterns.

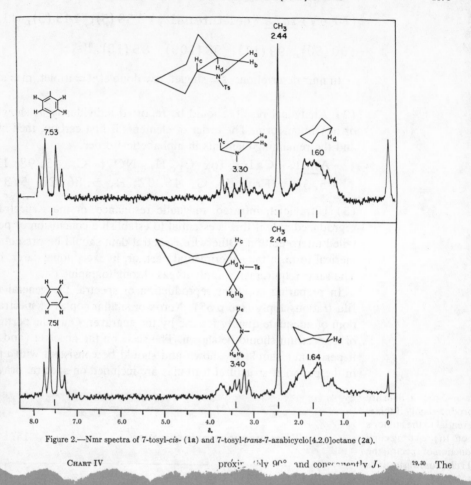

Figure 2.—Nmr spectra of 7-tosyl-*cis*- (1a) and 7-tosyl-*trans*-7-azabicyclo[4.2.0]octane (2a).

CHART IV   proxi... .'bly 90° and cons....ently *J*.... [29,30] The

FIGURE 5.—Spectral data should be planned for presentation on the printed page at exactly one- or two-column widths.

(4) Some types of data can be presented much more concisely in the running text than in tabular form. For instance, values of vapor pressure as a function of temperature can be given as a series of $[T \; (°K), P \; (mm)]$ values as in the example:

"Values of the vapor pressure of the compound, measured over a range of temperature, are [given as $\underline{T}$ (°K), $\underline{P}$ (mm)]: 175.5, 0.1; 189.7, 0.6; 209.8, 2.4; 228.1, 10.0; 250.4, 40.0; 273.3, 164.8; and 299.3, 382.4."

(5) Reports of crystal structure analyses should conform to recommendations of the Commission on Crystallographic Computing of the International Union of Crystallography [*Acta Cryst.,* **15,** 515 (1962)].

(6) Data from X-ray powder measurements should be accompanied by details of the experimental technique: the radiation, its wavelength, what filters were used, camera diameter, the type of X-ray recording, and the

technique for estimating intensities. Relevant information about the specimen used should be included. (Authors may wish to submit X-ray powder data to Dr. J. V. Smith, "A.S.T.M. X-Ray Powder Diffraction File," Department of Geophysical Sciences, University of Chicago, Chicago, Ill. 60637. Standard forms for reporting the data are obtainable from Mr. Arthur S. Beward, 1916 Race St., Philadelphia, Pa. 19103.)

MICROFILM AND PHOTOPRINT SUPPLEMENTS

By arrangement with the American Documentation Institute (ADI), supplementary material, such as extensive tables, graphs, spectra, and calculations, can be distributed in the form of microfilms with images 25 mm high on standard 35-mm film or 15×20 cm (6×8 in.) photoprints readable without optical aid. The supplementary material must be in a form easily handled for photoreproduction. If typewritten, a black ribbon should be used. Figures and illustrative material must be glossy prints. Although any size is acceptable, 22×28 cm (8.5×11 in.) is preferable.

In general this material should accompany the manuscript for review by the editors and reviewers. Upon acceptance, it will be sent by the editor to the American Documentation Institute where it is assigned a document number.

A deposit fee of $2 is required; it should be included with the material sent to the editor. The check must be made out to *Chief, Photoduplication Service, Library of Congress.*

The availability of the supplementary material should be noted in the paper with the following footnote:

A more detailed form of this paper (or extended version, or material supplementary to this article) has been deposited as Document No. 0000 with the ADI Auxiliary Publications Project, Photoduplication Service, Library of Congress, Washington, D. C. 20540. A copy may be secured by citing the document number and by remitting $0.00 for photoprints, or $0.00 for 35-mm microfilm. Advance payment is required. Make checks or money orders payable to: Chief, Photoduplication Service, Library of Congress.

The document number and the fees are inserted in the galley proof at the editorial office.

TABLES

A table may contain short descriptions or numerical listings. Tables should be self-explanatory and should supplement, not duplicate, the text and figures.

Relationships and comparisons are established by the correct choice of column heads (captions of vertical columns) and stubs (captions of horizontal rows). Numbers in a column are more easily compared than numbers in a line. If possible, items that are to be compared should be in the same column and in descending or ascending order of their rank.

When numerical data are presented in columns, the decimal points must be aligned. In numbers less than one, a zero should precede the decimal point. In some cases, multiplication of all entries in a column by some particular power of ten allows presentation of values in less space. The column should have, of course, an appropriate heading,

e.g., $10^4 \underline{k} (\sec^{-1})$.

Units of measurement, abbreviated, must be part of the column heading and should not be repeated in the body of the table. Ditto marks should not be used. *The inclusion of structural formulas in tables should be avoided.*

All data should be arranged compactly so as to occupy a minimum of space. The author should try to visualize his tables in type and foresee possible difficulties in setting. Arrangements which have excessive blank space should be avoided. Lengthy tables should be examined critically in an effort to reorganize and reduce them so that they can be fitted into the available space on a journal page.

Tables should be typed double-spaced, including all headings and footnotes. Ruled lines and brackets may be used in moderation, particularly after column heads and stubs, but they should never be included as a substitute for good alignment, adequate spacing, or clarity. Tables should be numbered consecutively with Roman numerals in the order in which they are first mentioned in the text, and each should have a brief title. Necessary explanatory material should be included in footnotes to the table. These notes are referred to by underlined, lower-case letters placed as superscripts and are listed consecutively as part of *each* table (see also p 70). All tables should be referred to in the text by their numbers. Whenever a table is mentioned in text, capitalize the first letter and spell out "Table."

e.g., as shown in Table III, additions of ....

TABLE I
MASS SPECTRUM OF $SF_5N{=}SF_2$
(IONIZATION VOLTAGE 75 v)

m/e	Intensity relative to SF_3^+	Ion	m/e	Intensity relative to SF_3^+	Ion
213	0.37	$NS^{34}S^{32}F_7^+$	90	1.05	
211	2.77[a]	$NS_2F_7^+$	89	100.0	SF_3^+
194	0.37	$NS^{34}S^{32}F_6^+$	86	0.74	$NS^{34}F_2^+$
192	2.40	$NS_2F_6^+$	84	5.37	NSF_2^+
154	0.61	$NS_2F_4^+$	79	0.31	
129	4.01	$S^{34}F_5^+$	72	1.30	$S^{34}F_2^+$
128	0.93		71	0.31	
127	84.5	SF_5^+	70	24.2	SF_2^+
108	2.68	SF_4^+	67	1.91	$NS^{34}F^+$
103	0.92	NSF_3^+	66	0.43	$N^{15}SF^+$
91	4.56	$S^{34}F_3^+$	65	25.4	NSF^+

[a] Parent peak.

FIGURE 6.—Good alignment, adequate spacing, and clarity are prerequisites for all tables to be published in the journals.

Short tables consisting of not more than three lines and four columns may be run directly into the text by means of an introductory sentence. These tables do not have titles, nor are they numbered.

Tables containing many data occupy much less space if they are reproduced directly from a photoreduction of a clear, typed, or computer-printed table. Some editors encourage use of such tables for presentation of structure factor data from single crystal diffraction studies. There are other types of data also, *e.g.,* potentiometric data in stability constant studies, where such concise, but readable, presentation is appropriate. The proportions of such tables should be such that they will fit in one- or two-column widths. See Figure 7 for an example of such a photoreduced table of structure factor data.

TABLE I

OBSERVED AND CALCULATED STRUCTURE FACTORS FOR $(C_6H_5)_4AsRuCl_4(H_2O)_2 \cdot H_2O$

FIGURE 7.—For some types of data tables reproduced directly from photoreduction of a clear, typed, or computer-printed table are acceptable.

Data which may be useful to future workers but are not treated theoretically or do not form a major topic of discussion in the manuscript should not be presented in table form. Such material is often best handled by running it into the text. Examples are ir absorptions and nmr chemical shifts. Lengthy and detailed supplementary material should be submitted for deposition with the ADI Auxiliary Publications Project (see p 57).

STRUCTURAL FORMULAS

Freehand drawing of organic structures is seldom acceptable; templates and stencils should be used (see below and p 102). The Rapidograph pen, point No. 0 is recommended for drawing bonds, arrows, benzene rings, and the many variations of geometrical designs which are encountered in structures.

The importance of presenting neat and clear displays can hardly be overemphasized. Special attention should be given to correctness of symbols, location of subscripts, superscripts, and ionic charges, and to the placing and joining of bond lines.

Structural formulas should be prepared with care and also with a view to the most economical use of space. All structures should be numbered consecutively from left to right, top to bottom *in boldface Arabic numerals,* regardless of the order in which the compounds occur in the text. Repetition of the same structure should be avoided; the number of an earlier structure may be used alone if a compound occurs several times.

Structural formulas are usually redrawn by the printer with standard size rings (12 mm) and lettering (4 mm) in manuscripts for *Biochemistry, Chemical Reviews, Inorganic Chemistry,* the *Journal of the American Chemical Society,* the *Journal of Medicinal Chemistry, The Journal of Organic Chemistry,* and *The Journal of Physical Chemistry.* Xerox copies of these drawings are sent with proofs; after any corrections are made, the display is reduced for reproduction.

The author should arrange structural formulas in horizontal rows so that the display or block will fill a single column width or, for very large groups, an entire page width. If this is not done, it may be necessary to rearrange the display, with possible loss of clarity, to avoid waste of space in the journal page. The following points will help the author adjust formula layouts to these sizes.

(1) A single column width will accommodate 13 contiguous six-membered rings or an equivalent amount of linear structures.

(2) Three letters (in a side chain or above an arrow) are approximately equivalent to one ring.

(3) A bond line to a side chain is half the width of a ring.

(4) Subscript numbers require half a letter width.

(5) For clarity, a space equivalent to one ring width should be left between formulas.

(6) Symbols on arrows between formulas should be as brief and compact as possible. Abbreviations such as Me for CH_3, Et for C_2H_5, Ph (not ϕ) for C_6H_5 are desirable in manuscripts in the field of organic chemistry.

If the author uses a 12-mm ring size in his drawings and the allowances given for lettering, side chains, and spaces, the material in a 17-cm column (normal typed page) in the manuscript will fit into one column in the printed page. This ring size is No. 16 on the Rapidesign No. 50 Pocket Pal template or No. 11 on the Fieser Chemist's Triangle.

If it is necessary to arrange structures for a full-page width, a 36-cm width drawing is possible with 12-mm rings. If a satisfactory arrangement is slightly larger than the limits for a one-column presentation, it is preferable to stagger or overlap structures in successive rows rather than spread out the display to a full page. In multi-ring structures such as steroids, partial structures showing only the pertinent points are encouraged. For examples of finished formula layouts see Figures 8 and 9.

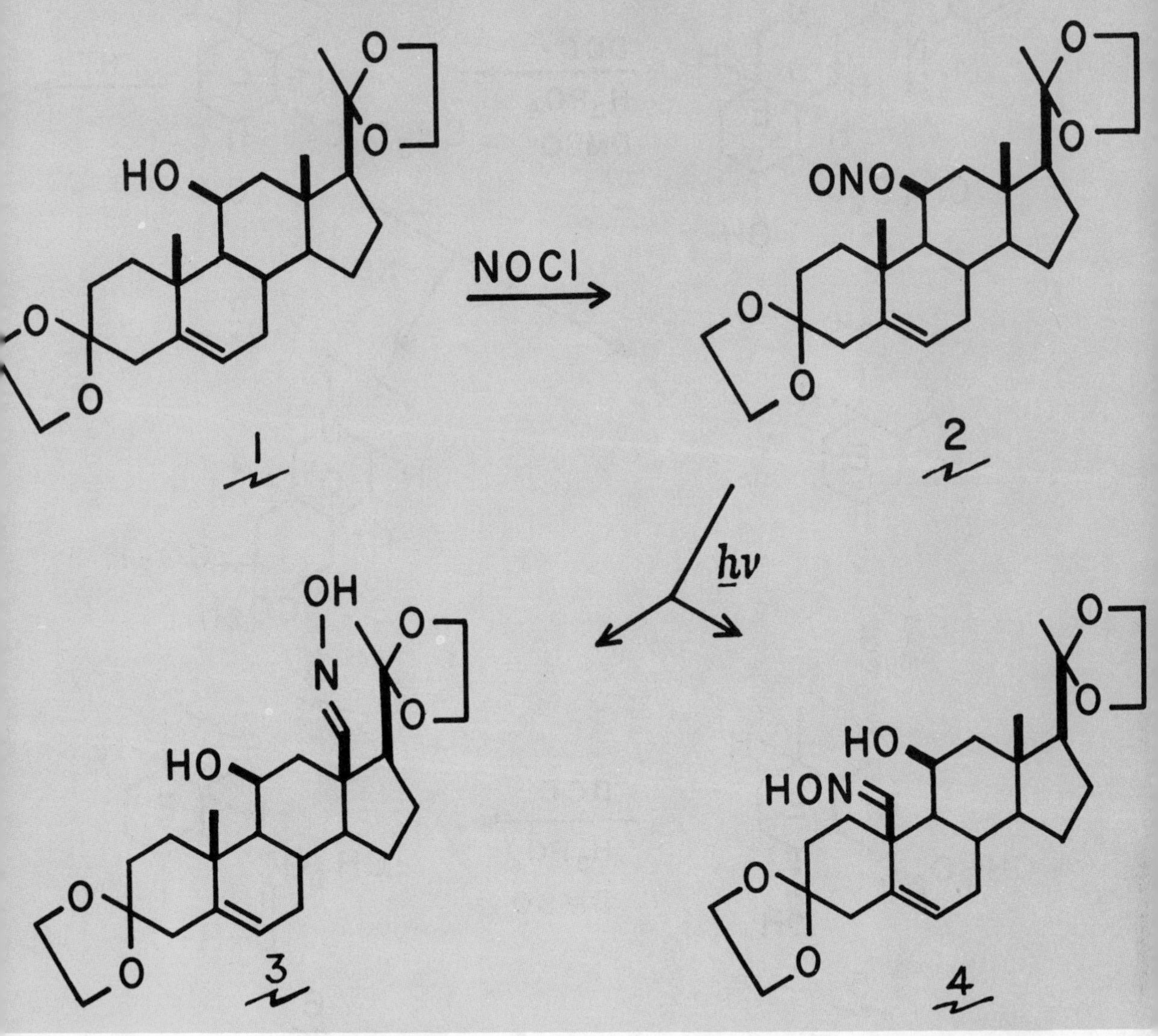

FIGURE 8.—Example of a formula layout as submitted by the author and, to the right, it is reproduced in the journal. The presentation is compact and planned for one-column width; structures are numbered consecutively in boldface Arabic numerals.

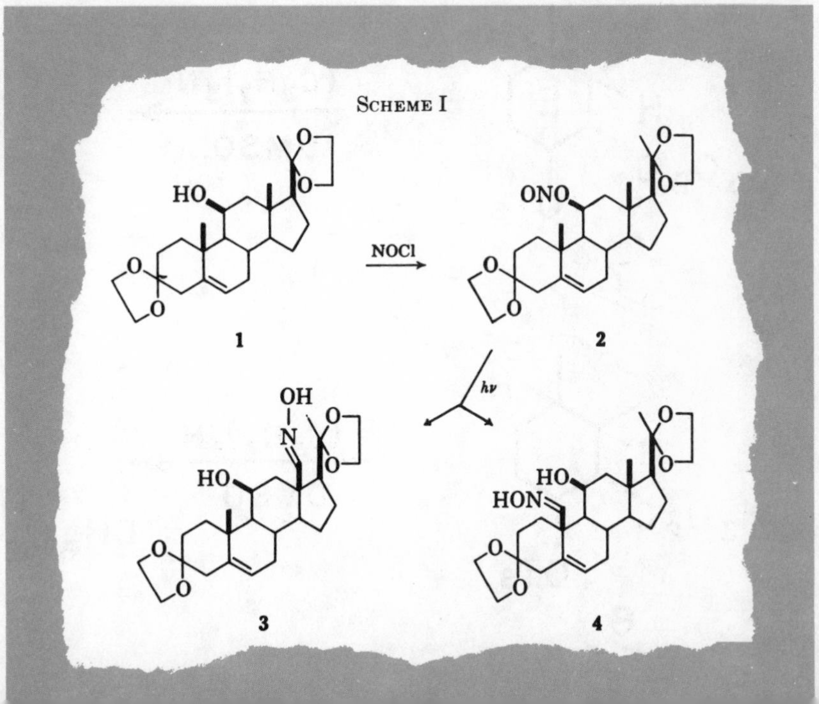

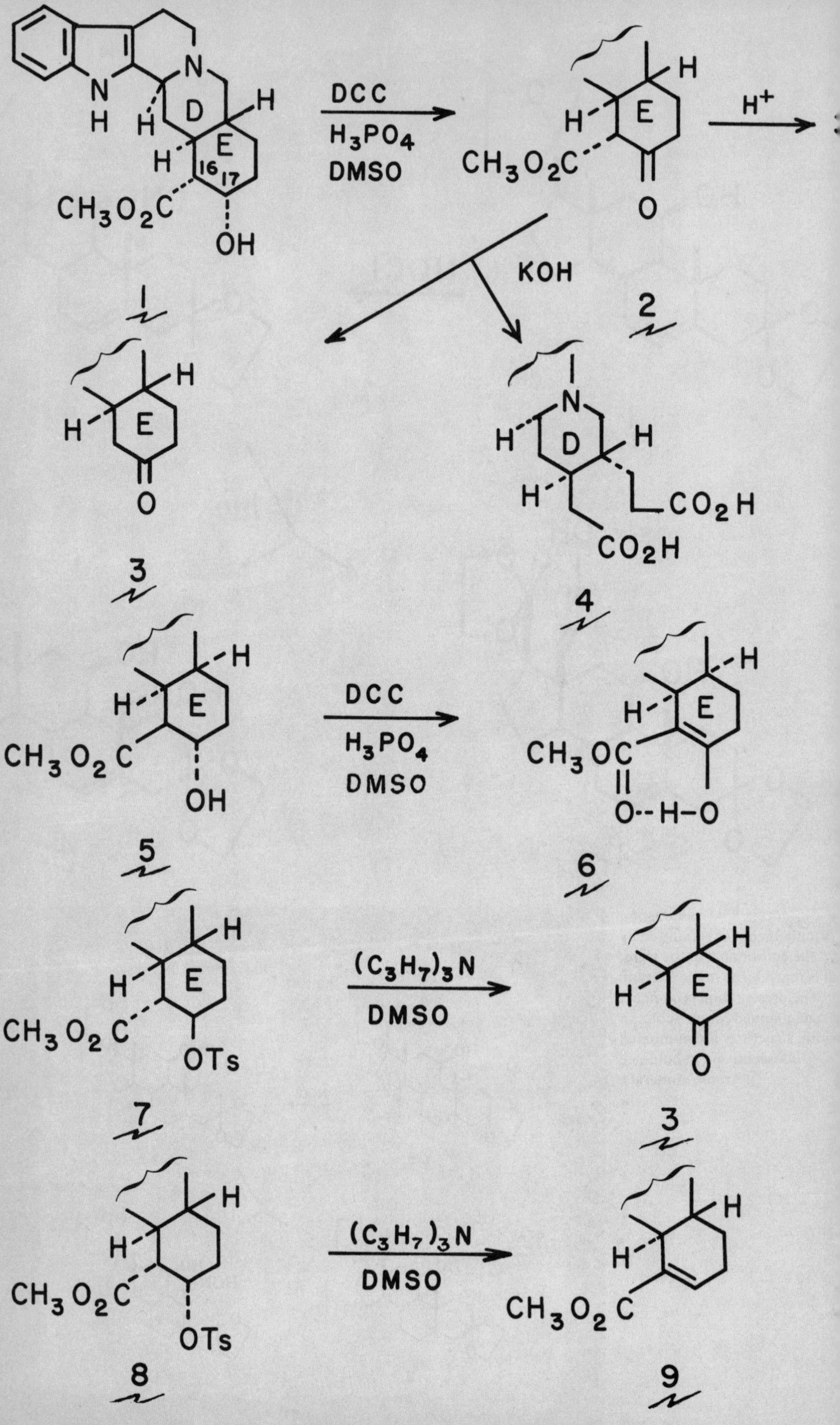

1

$\xrightarrow{\text{DCC}}{\text{H}_3\text{PO}_4}{\text{DMSO}}$

$\xrightarrow{\text{H}^+}$

2

KOH

3

4

$\xrightarrow{\text{DCC}}{\text{H}_3\text{PO}_4}{\text{DMSO}}$

5

6

$\xrightarrow{(\text{C}_3\text{H}_7)_3\text{N}}{\text{DMSO}}$

7

3

$\xrightarrow{(\text{C}_3\text{H}_7)_3\text{N}}{\text{DMSO}}$

8

9

FIGURE 9.—Formula layout, to the left, as submitted by the author and, to the right, as it appeared in the journal. Note the use of partial structures.

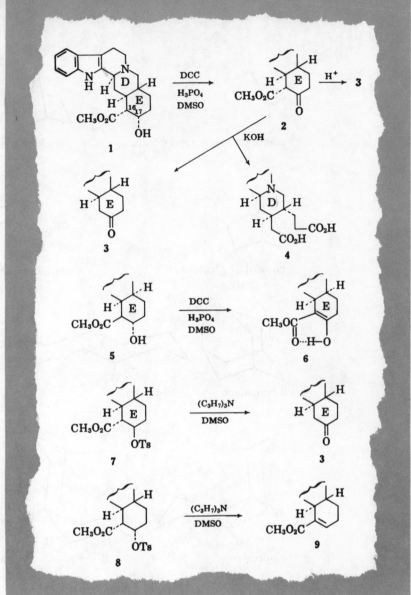

In structural layouts involving odd-shaped rings, bicyclic structures, etc., it is important that these structures be drawn exactly as they are to appear in the journal. They should also be consistent throughout, since all of the structures in a given manuscript may not be redrawn by the same person. Any special features or important points in structural drawings should be clearly indicated on the manuscript.

Although fairly complicated structures can be redrawn in the standard format, very complex formulas or drawings in which perspective is crucial may be better submitted as copy suitable for direct photographic preparation of an engraving. It is not necessary to provide such copy for standard structural formula layouts. In preparing engraver's copy of complex drawings, the same general points and requirements for lettering size apply that are discussed for illustrations.

In drawing structural formulas the author should strive to reach the best possible representation of molecular geometry. The following examples have been drawn with the aid of the L. F. Fieser's "Chemist's Triangle" template.

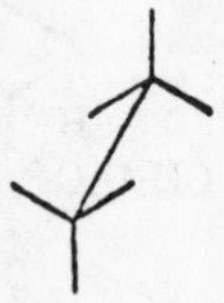

ethane (sawhorse representation)

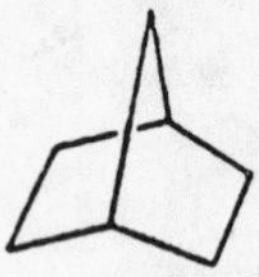

bicyclo [2.2.1] heptane

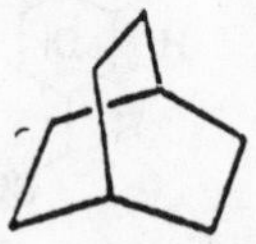

bicyclo[2.2.2] octane

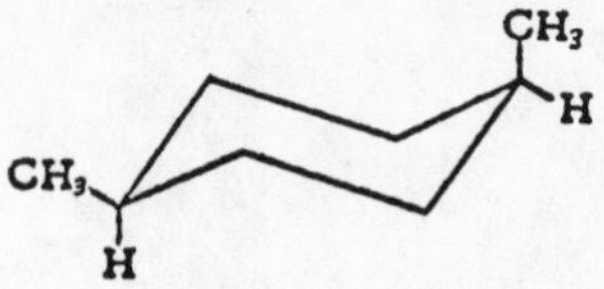

cis-1,4-dimethylcyclohexane (chair)

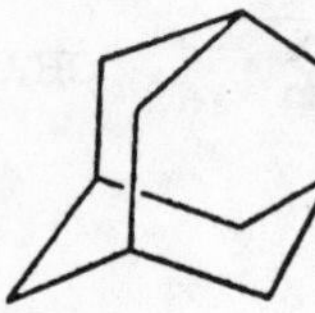

adamantane

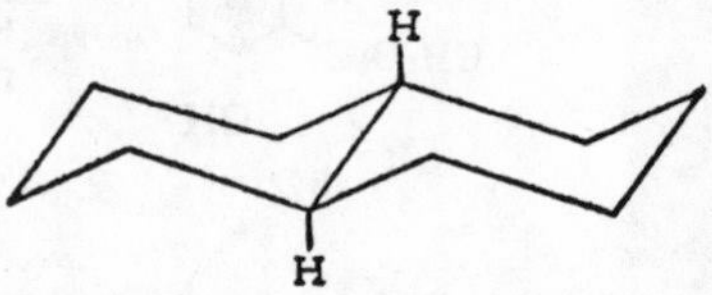

trans-decalin

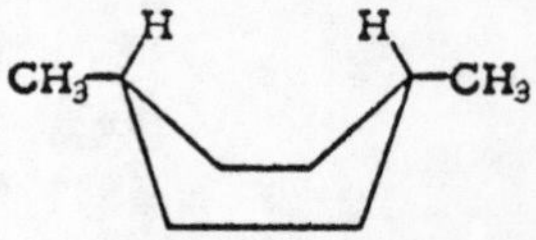

cis-1,4-dimethylcyclohexane
(extreme boat)

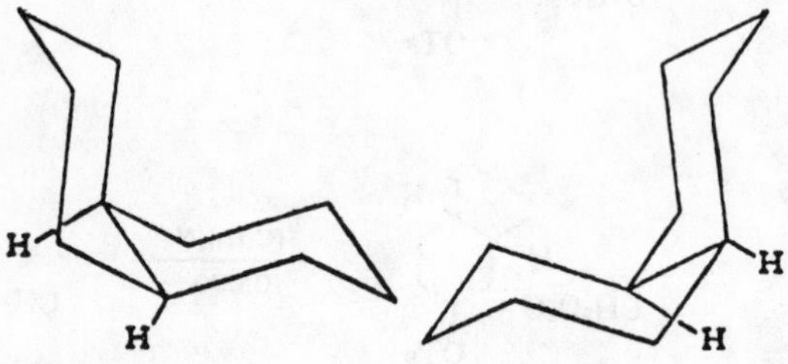

cis-decalin

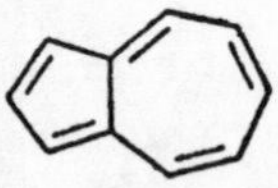

azulene

ferrocene

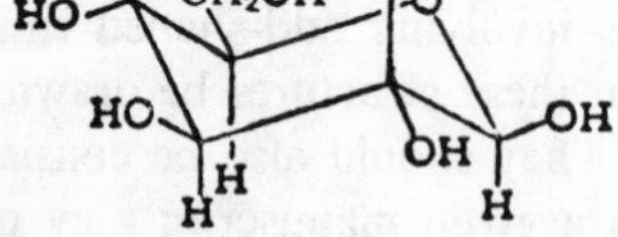

β-D-glucose

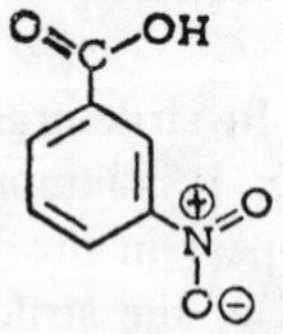

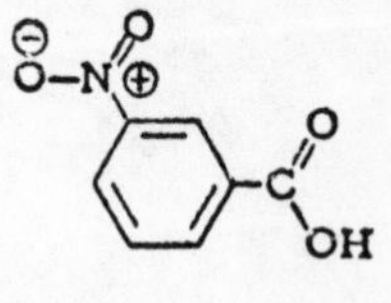

m-nitrobenzoic acid

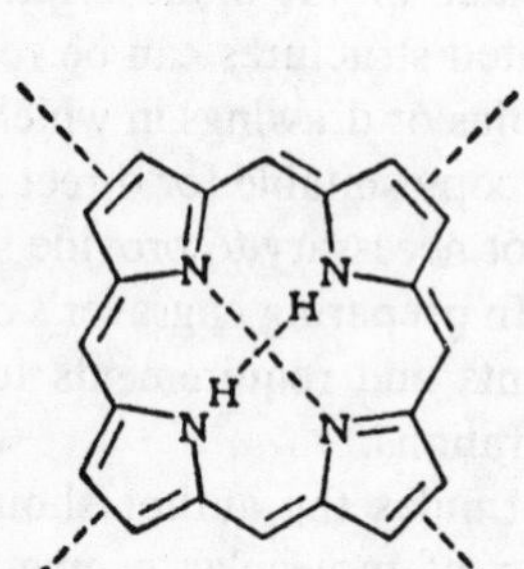

porphyrin (note construction
lines to locate N atoms)

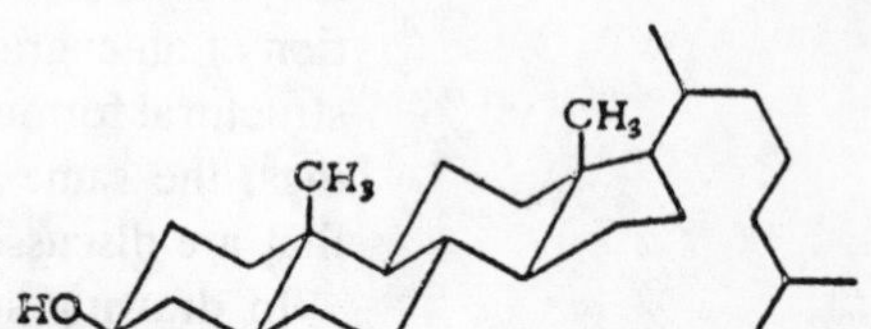

cholestanol

In three-dimensional drawings of chemical structures, the lines in the background that are crossed by lines in the foreground should be broken to give a greater three-dimensional effect. Also, lines in the foreground can be made heavier. Two examples follow:

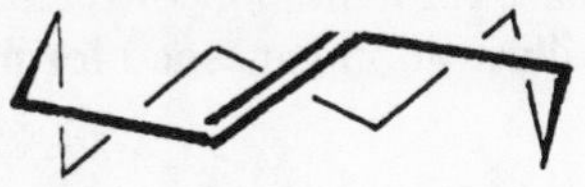

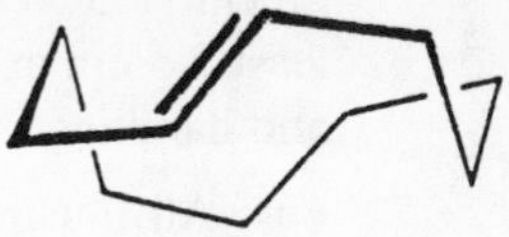

Special care is needed in representing steroid systems. For example, substances like cholestanol, having side chains, can be very effectively done with a template according to the following scheme:

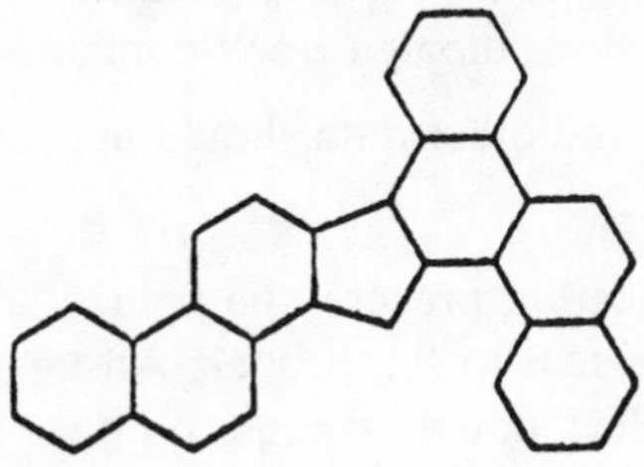

Step 1 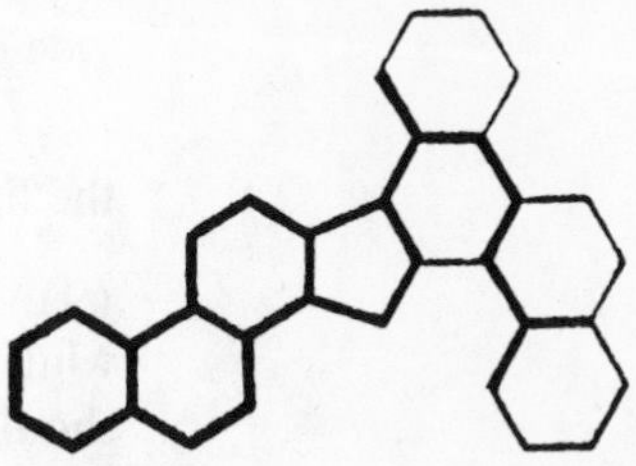   Step 2

Step 3

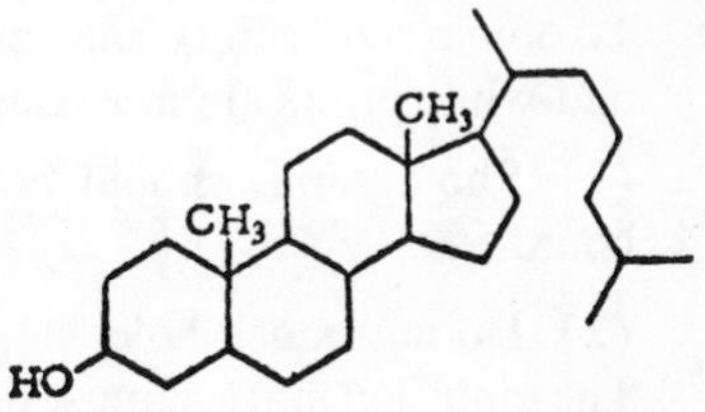

For simple displays of chemical formulas, the symbols may be typed. In such cases a preliminary sketch in light blue pencil is very helpful as a guide for typing the chemical symbols in the correct locations of structures. The inking is done (with the aid of a template) after all the typed symbols are in place. Bonds should not run into the chemical symbols. Dots, angles, and bonds should be evenly spaced and aligned. (See also *Hints to the Typist*, Appendix 4).

ILLUSTRATIONS

Illustrations should be included only when they substantially increase understanding of the text. *Authors must submit accurate, clear, and well-proportioned illustrations.* Failure of an illustration to meet the requirements of editors and engravers usually means a delay in publication of the manuscript. Recommendations for the presentation and submission of illustrations accompanying manuscripts are listed below:

(1) A set of illustrations must be included with each copy of the manuscript.

(2) Original art work or glossy, positive photographic prints must be submitted with the original copy; clear reproductions may be submitted with the duplicate copies.

(3) The originals should be marked in pencil on the back with the name

of the author(s) and the title of the article for efficient identification during handling by the editors, printer, and photoengraver.

(4) Art work offered for reproduction should never be folded.

(5) Whenever practicable, original illustrations should be drawn on 22 × 28 cm (8.5 × 11 in.) sheets for handling convenience. A clear space of at least 2.5 cm around the illustration is needed for markings, identification, and handling.

(6) All illustrations should be numbered in sequence, with Arabic numerals, in order of appearance in the text. Number as Figure 1, Figure 2, etc. Do not use terms such as "Chart" or "Plate."

(7) Every figure must have a caption that includes the figure number and a brief, informative title. If more information is needed, use complete sentences and standard punctuation. If possible, the caption should provide enough detail to make the figure self-contained.

(8) Keys to symbols and other data should appear in the caption, not in the figure itself.

(9) During the publication process, the figures are sent to the engraver while the captions are sent to the printer. All figure captions, therefore, should be typed together, double-spaced, on a separate page.

PHOTOGRAPHS To obtain satisfactory half-tone reproductions high-contrast, glossy, black-and-white prints are most desirable.

(1) Photographs should be mailed flat, well protected by heavy cardboard.

(2) Do not punch holes in photographs or fasten them with metal clips. The emulsion surface must be free of irregularities and markings.

(3) Each print should be clearly labeled on the back with a *soft* pencil, giving the name of the author(s), title of the manuscript, and figure number, and indicating which edge is the top of the illustration.

DRAWINGS AND GRAPHS Uniformity should be maintained in all art work prepared for a single manuscript. Freehand or typewritten lettering should not be used. Note the recommendations in this handbook for symbols and abbreviations to be used on diagrams. The suggestions that follow are guides to the preparation of charts and drawings that can be reproduced in journals.*

(1) A good illustration is clear and simple; reduce lines and wording to a minimum.

(2) Avoid showing more than three or four curves on one illustration.

(3) Avoid interlaced or unrelated curves.

(4) If possible, design illustrations for printing to fit the width of one column, usually about 8.5 cm. The original drawing should be twice the publication size, that is 17 cm. The height of the drawing will vary to meet individual requirements. Reproduced illustrations *wider* than column

---

*Information on the preparation of illustrations to be made into slides and on the production and use of visual aids for the presentation of a paper may be found in ACS Bulletin 8, "Suggestions on how to organize, present, and illustrate a technical paper," American Chemical Society, Washington, D. C. (1961).

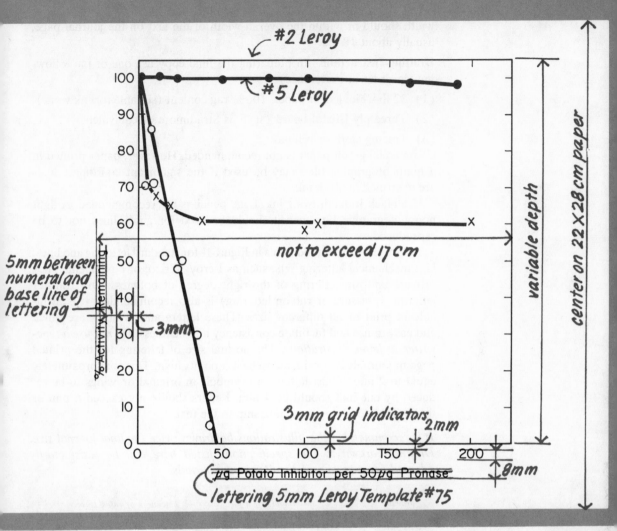

#2 Leroy

#5 Leroy

100
90
80
70
60
50
40
30
20
10
0

% Activity Remaining

5mm between numeral and base line of lettering

3mm

not to exceed 17 cm

variable depth

center on 22×28 cm paper

3mm grid indicators 2mm

8mm

0   50   100   150   200

μg Potato Inhibitor per 50μg Pronase

lettering 5mm Leroy Template #75

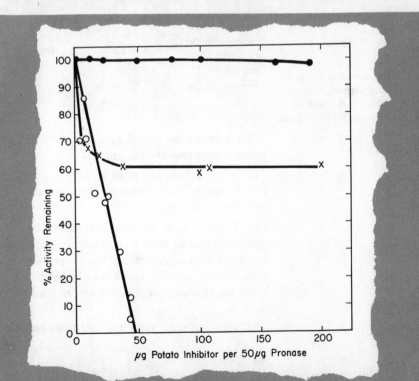

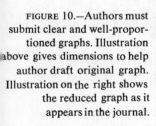

FIGURE 10.—Authors must submit clear and well-proportioned graphs. Illustration above gives dimensions to help author draft original graph. Illustration on the right shows the reduced graph as it appears in the journal.

100
90
80
70
60
50
40
30
20
10
0

% Activity Remaining

0   50   100   150   200

μg Potato Inhibitor per 50μg Pronase

width should fit within the overall width of the text on the journal page, usually about 18 cm.

Drafting Instructions—In preparing the final copy use one of the following (in order of preference):

(1) 32 lb white ledger paper, 100% rag content (suitable for ink work).

(2) Three-ply Bristol board (such as Strathmore or equivalent).

(3) Tracing cloth or vellum.

Commercial graph paper is not recommended. However, paper printed in a nonphotographic blue may be used if the significant coordinate lines are overruled in black ink.

Use black India drawing ink. Lead pencil is not recommended. A light nonphotographic blue pencil should be used for guide lines not to be reproduced.

Follow the recommendations in Figure 11 for standard lettering and lines. Use mechanical lettering sets, such as Leroy, Wrico, or equivalent. They provide uniform lettering of the right degree of boldness. Dry transfer lettering (pressure or rub-on lettering) is also recommended; it is available in print of all different sizes. These letters and symbols are quick and easy to use and facilitate consistency and neatness. *Do not use a typewriter to letter illustrations.* The normal size of lettering for the printed page in journals is considered to be 4.5 points high. This is approximately equal to 2 mm. Thus, letters and symbols in original drawings to be reduced by one-half should be 4 mm. Letters should not exceed 6 mm or they will be too large in relationship to the text.

It is recommended that illustrations be drawn twice the final journal size. Originals drawn to the specifications listed here can be satisfactorily adapted for any one of the Research journals.

Width of drawing	Minimum height for:			Thickness of ruled lines
To fit single text column in journal: 17 cm	Lower case letters	Numerals & capital letters	Symbols within drawings	Light, #1 Leroy _____ for graph grids, bonds, arrows
To fit double text column in journal: 36 cm	3 mm	4 mm	3 mm	Medium, #2 Leroy _____ for graph borders or reference lines Heavy, #5 Leroy ▬▬ for graph curves or emphasis lines

FIGURE 11.—Standard sizes for lines and lettering to be used by authors in the drafting of original illustrations.

To improve the visual appearance of line graphs the following additional suggestions are presented:

(1) A ruled open-grid must be used if quantitative reference to the figure is to be made. Tick marks may be employed if only semiquantitative presentation is desired.

(2) The grid scale for each axis should be chosen thoughtfully with full understanding of how the choice of grid proportion affects the plotted curves. A well-designed grid has proportions that show the picture properly, and the number and kind of rulings that help the reader to understand the character of the data and to read the curve with the desired exactness.

(3) Show all scale numbers and titles outside the grid border.

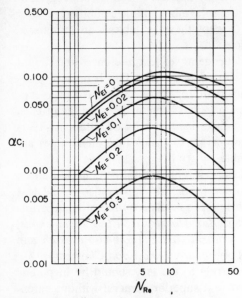

Figure 7. Effect of surface tension on growth rate for most unstable wave

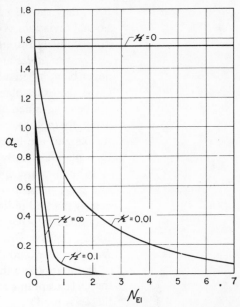

Figure 18. Effect of diffusion on critical wave number for $N_{Re} = 1$

FIGURE 12.—Examples of clear, one-column graphs. The type of grid and grid scales to be used must be chosen thoughtfully by the author.

(4) The axes must be labeled clearly with both the quantity measured and the units in which it is measured.

(5) Each caption should be parallel to its axis.

(6) All lettering and numbers should read from left to right if possible, or from bottom to top if necessary

(7) For plot-points, use template data symbols. Avoid small, illegible freehand variety. Height of symbols should not exceed 4 mm.

The following symbols are recommended in the order of preference: ●, ▲, ■, ◆, ▼, ✕, +, ○, △, □, ◇, ▽.

(8) No lines should pass through any lettering or symbols.

FORMAT FOR DOCUMENTATION

FOOTNOTES   There are two kinds of footnotes, those of content and those of reference. *Content footnotes* provide a place for material that the writer wishes to include in his report but which would disrupt the flow of thought if introduced into the text. They are used to amplify or to qualify textual discussion and to make acknowledgments. Most journals discourage the use of content footnotes. *Reference footnotes* are used in some journals to cite the authority for statements in the text—specific facts or opinions as well as exact quotations. These footnotes are also used for cross references to other parts of the work.

The place in the text at which a footnote is introduced is generally marked with a superior numeral (an Arabic numeral elevated slightly above the line) set after all punctuation. These numerals should follow the passage to which they refer; to avoid possible misunderstanding, however, they should not be placed after a symbol, another number, or after an abbreviation. *All* footnotes (except those in tables) are numbered consecutively throughout an article.*

Notes to tables are handled independently of text references and should never be numbered in sequence with text footnotes. This is necessary because the exact place where a table will appear on the printed page cannot be determined until the journal page has been made up by the printer. Table footnotes are referred to by underlined, lower-case letters as superscripts and are listed consecutively as part of *each* table. The notes are then placed directly under the table.

In the manuscript text footnotes preferably should be collected all on one page in proper numerical order (with first appearance in the text clearly marked in the margin); this is specifically required of manuscripts submitted to *Analytical Chemistry, Biochemistry, I&EC Fundamentals, I&EC Process Design and Development, I&EC Product Research and Development,* and the *Journal of Agricultural and Food Chemistry.*

In the footnote the numeral referring to the text should be in parentheses (except in *Biochemistry,* where a superior numeral without parentheses is used).

REFERENCES Practice varies among the journals in the placing of bibliographic references.

Accounts of Chemical Research, Analytical Chemistry, Chemical Reviews, Inorganic Chemistry, the *Journal of the Americal Chemical Society,* the *Journal of Medicinal Chemistry, The Journal of Organic Chemistry,* and *The Journal of Physical Chemistry* publish references as footnotes at the bottom of each page.

Advances in Chemistry Series, Biochemistry, Environmental Science and Technology, I&EC Fundamentals, I&EC Process Design and Development, I&EC Product Research and Development, the *Journal of Agricultural and Food Chemistry,* and the *Journal of Chemical Documentation* cite references in the text as follows:

one author: (Smith, 1945)

one author with several references in a single year: (Smith, 1945a, b, ... etc.)

more than two authors: (Smith et al., 1961)

and then list the references alphabetically according to author at the end of the paper under the heading "References."

Industrial and Engineering Chemistry lists references at the end of the paper, in alphabetical order according to author. They are then numbered consecutively, and the appropriate number (in parentheses on the line) is used to indicate references in the text.

The *Journal of Chemical and Engineering Data* accepts and publishes references in any one of the forms acceptable to the other Society journals.

When listing references as footnotes, do not assign a new number to the same reference each time it is cited. When more than one reference is

---

*In *Biochemistry,* footnotes to title and by-line are indicated by reference marks (*, †, ‡, //, #, **, ...). Footnotes to the text are then numbered consecutively.

of *A. obscurinervium* Az... ...aspido-
ethanol[5] and the basic portion of th... ...carbonyl function (1750
tioned between benzene and dilute acetic acid. The ...he mass spectra of the alkaloids (Fig. 1)
latter fraction contained (+)-aspidocarpine (Ia)[6–8] showed a diagnostic and exceedingly simple pattern,
in a very high yield (3.5% of the ethanol extract), (+)- with the only significant peaks arising from loss of
aspidolimine (Ib, 0.025%),[7,9] and a new alkaloid of the methyl and carbon monoxide (from all four molecular
methoxyindole type (0.5%) whose structure is currently ions) and ethyl (from the molecular ions of IIa and IIb
under investigation. The former fraction (benzene- only); small peaks were also present at m/e 244 (in all
soluble acetates) contained four closely related bases: four spectra and unaffected by catalytic deuteration
dihydroobscurinervine (IIa, 0.06%), obscurinervine of the 6,7 double bond; ion a), 260 (IIa and IIb; ion
(IIb, 0.07%), dihydroobscurinervidine (IIc, 0.01%), f), and 246 (IIc and IId; ion c).[11,12a] The molecular
and obscurinervidine (IId, 0.03%). These were as- ion peaks (IIa, m/e 440 = $C_{25}H_{32}N_2O_5$; IIb, m/e 438 =
signed the unusual heptacyclic constitutions on the $C_{25}H_{30}N_2O_5$; IIc, m/e 426 = $C_{24}H_{30}N_2O_5$; IId, m/e
basis of the evidence described below. 424 = $C_{24}H_{28}N_2O_5$) confirmed the formulas indicated
by analysis, and led to a simplification of the picture
confirmed by hydrogenation of IIb to IIa, and IId to
IIc. Also implied in the mass spectra was the conclusion that the obscurinervine and obscurinervidine pairs
differed only in the presence of an easily expelled ethyl
group in the former, replaced by a methyl group in the
latter, probably attached to the aromatic portion of
the molecules.

(1) Part XLV: J. A. Joule and C. Djerassi, *J. Chem. Soc.*, in press.

(2) Partial support was provided by the National Institutes of Health (Grant No. GM-11309) of the U. S. Public Health Service.

(3) National Institutes of Health Postdoctorate Fellow, 1963.

(4) For most recent reference on this work, see J. M. Ferreira, B. Gilbert, R. J. Owellen, and C. Djerassi, *Experientia*, **19**, 585 (1963).

(5) We thank Dr. B. Gilbert, Universidade do Brasil, Rio de Janeiro, for the collection and initial extraction of the bark, which was collected 8 km. north of Manaus, Amazonas. Thanks are due to Dr. W. Rodrigues for locating this tree.

(6) S. McLean, K. Palmer, and L. Marion, *Can. J. Chem.*, **38**, 1547 (1960).

(7) Identity was established by infrared and ultraviolet spectra, optical rotation, and a mixture melting point with an authentic sample of the compound.

(8) The configurations of all compounds in this paper are relative and not absolute.

(9) H. Schmid and M. Pinar, *Helv. Chim. Acta*, **45**, 1283 (1962); B. Gilbert, J. A. Brissolese, J. M. Wilson, H. Budzikiewicz, L. J. Durham, and C. Djerassi, *Chem. Ind.* (London), 1949 (1962).

(10) C. Djerassi, L. D. Antonaccio, H. Budzikiewicz, J. M. Wilson, and B. Gilbert, *Tetrahedron Letters*, 1001 (1962).

(11) For reasons explained in H. Budzikiewicz, C. Djerassi, and D. H. Williams, "Interpretation of Mass Spectra of Organic Compounds," Holden-Day, Inc., San Francisco, Calif., 1964, we are fixing the charge on nitrogen in molecular ions, followed by homolytic cleavages in all cases, to give ions in which the charge is also localized.

(12) (a) We thank Dr. H. Budzikiewicz and Mr. J. Smith for the mass spectral determinations. (b) We are indebted to Dr. L. Durham and Mr. T. Burkoth for the n.m.r. determinations.

FIGURE 13.—Examples of format for listing references. Illustration above shows style preferred by journals that publish references as footnotes at the bottom of each page. Illustration below shows style preferred by journals that list references at the end of each paper.

...ion of human ...
...contains fucose, galactose, N-acetylglu... ...pre... ...ntermediate s...
amine, and N-acetylgalactosamine in a molar ratio of the oligosaccharide units in ac... ...ce with
of approximately 2:2:1:2 (Table IV). If all the oligo- scheme formulated by Watkins and Morgan (1959).
saccharide units from which the terminal N-acetyl-
galactosamine residues are enzymatically removed are
structurally identical, each of them will contain two

fucose, two galactose, one N-acetylglucosamine, and **References**
two N-acetylgalactosamine residues. The results are
compatible with a simple sequence of N-acetylhexos- Annison, E. F., and Morgan, W. T. J. (1952), *Biochem.*
amine and galactose units, as proposed by Rege *et al.* *J. 52,* 247.
(1963) Baer, H., Dische, Z., and Kabat, E. A. (1948), *J. Exptl.*
Med. 88, 59.
Bendich, A., Kabat, E. A., and Bezer, A. E. (1946),
J. Exptl. Med. 83, 485.

α-GalNAc-(1–3)-β-Gal-(1→3 or 4)-
β-GlcNAc-(1–3)-β-Gal-(1–3)-GalNAc-

Boyd, W. C., and Shapleigh, E. (1954), *J. Lab. Clin.*
Med. 44, 235.
to which two α-L-fucose residues are laterally attached. Côté, R. H., and Morgan, W. T. J. (1956), *Nature 178,*
The destruction of A specificity by the snail enzyme 1171.
was accompanied by a significant enhancement of Dische, Z. (1955), *Methods Biochem. Analy. 2,* 313.
H activity. Similar observations have been made by Freudenberg, K., and Eichel, H. (1935), *Ann. 518,* 97.
Harrap and Watkins (1964) using the *T. foetus* enzyme György, P., Rose, C. S., and Springer, G. F. (1954),
J. Lab. Clin. Med. 43, 543.

1746

HANS TUPPY AND WALTER L. STAUDENBAUER

cited at a given place, the numbers should be listed in the text in series and separated by commas except where there are three or more consecutive numbers, in which case the first and last numbers are separated by a hyphen.

To avoid unnecessary repetition in reference footnotes, the abbreviation *ibid.* for *ibidem,* "in the same place," may be used to replace journal abbreviations that are identical in consecutive notes. For instance:

(1) C. D. Doe, <u>J. Amer. Chem. Soc.</u>, 72, 1200 (1950).

(2) A. B. Roe, <u>ibid.</u>, 75, 500 (1953).

Ibid. is never used in those journals that cite references in the text by author name rather than by a number (see p 70). The terms *loc. cit., op. cit., idem,* are not used in any of the journals.

The author is responsible for the accuracy and completeness of all references in his paper. *All parts of a reference listing should be checked against the original document.* A reference must include certain minimum data, as follows:

Journals—Author, journal, volume, initial page, year.

  Books—Author, title, publisher, city of publication, year, chapter or page(s).

In *Advances in Chemistry Series, Biochemistry, Environmental Science and Technology, I&EC Fundamentals, I&EC Process Design and Development, I&EC Product Research and Development,* the *Journal of Agricultural and Food Chemistry,* and the *Journal of Chemical Documentation* these data should be arranged as follows:

Journals—Author, year, journal, volume, initial page.

  Books—Author, year, title, city of publication, publisher, chapter or page(s).

For other material enough information must be provided so that the material can be identified and located. Publications such as company records that are not considered part of the permanent literature should not be included.

Below are examples of bibliographic references most frequently used as they should appear in the typed manuscript. The information that must be supplied, the order of appearance for each item, points of style, such as underscoring, punctuation, and capitalization, are indicated. Recent issues of the journals should be consulted for individual style preferences.

REFERENCES TO JOURNALS In *footnotes* the author's initials appear before the surname. In *reference lists* published at the end of the text the surname is followed by initials. The names of all authors should be given.

The name of the journal, abbreviated according to the Chemical Abstracts Service *Guide for Abbreviating Periodical Titles* and the *Chemical Abstracts List of Periodicals** (see also Appendix 7), should be underlined to denote italics, and a wavy line under the volume number should

---

*Beginning in 1967 new periodical title abbreviations are being used by the Chemical Abstracts Service in its publications. The *Guide for Abbreviating Periodical Titles* has been prepared to help in converting the periodical title abbreviations used by *Chemical*

be used to denote boldface type.

(1) A. B. Smith, J. Amer. Chem. Soc. , 85, 1234 (1963).

For journals in which no boldface type is used, both journal title and volume number should be underlined.

Smith, A. B. (1963), J. Amer. Chem. Soc. 85, 1234.

(2) A. B. Smith, C. D. Roe, and B. C. Doe, J. Phys. Chem. , 64, 104 (1960).

(3) R. Doe and C. Roe, J. Chem. Soc. , 112 (1960).

(4) R. Doe, J. Chem. Soc. , Sect. C, 90 (1966).

References to journals that begin every issue with page one should include the issue number in parentheses following the volume number.

(5) A. B. Doe, Chem. Eng. News, 44 (41), 23 (1966).

When reference is made to an abstract of an article, this should be indicated. If possible, references for both the original article and the abstract should be given.

(6) C. D. Roe, Zh. Fiz. Khim. , 50, 1234 (1963); Chem. Abstr. , 56, 112a (1963).

Abstracts prior to 1967 to those recommended by the "American Standard for Periodical Title Abbreviations," ASA Z39.5-1963. The *Guide* is available at $1.50 per copy from the Chemical Abstracts Service, The Ohio State University, Columbus, Ohio 43210.

Words to be abbreviated in periodical titles should be determined from the *1961 Chemical Abstracts List of Periodicals with Key to Library Files* and its 1962, 1963, 1964, 1965, and January 1966 - June 1967 Supplements. However, because some of the American Standard periodical title word abbreviations differ from those used in the *CA List of Periodicals*, words should be checked also in the Chemical Abstracts Service *Guide for Abbreviating Periodical Titles*.

The 1961 *Chemical Abstracts List of Periodicals* (approximately 8150 periodicals) with a key to library files (334 libraries) and other information appeared as a part of the 1961 *Chemical Abstracts Author and Numerical Patent Index*. Supplements to this 1961 *List of Periodicals* appeared as a part of the Vol. 57 (July-Dec, 1962), Vol. 59 (July-Dec, 1963), Vol. 61 (July-Dec, 1964), Vol. 63 (July-Dec, 1965), and Vol. 66 (Jan-June, 1967) *Author and Numerical Patent Index*. Reprints of the 1961 *List* are available at $5.00 per copy. Reprints of the 1962, 1963, 1964, 1965, or 1966-1967 Supplements are available at $2.00 per copy. Orders should be sent to Special Issues Sales, American Chemical Society, 1155 Sixteenth Street, N.W., Washington, D. C. 20036.

Beginning in 1969, periodical titles will be abbreviated according to the *Comprehensive List of Periodicals for Chemistry and Chemical Engineering*, Chemical Abstracts Service, Columbus, Ohio (in preparation).

Reference to the English translation of a foreign journal should, if possible, also include reference to the original article.

(7) A. B. Doe, Zh. Obshch. Khim., 30, 2100 (1960); J. Gen. Chem. USSR, 30, 2050 (1960).

REFERENCES TO BOOKS

(8) A. B. Doe, "Textbook of Chemistry," 3rd ed, C. D. Jones and Co., New York, N. Y., 1962, p 123.

In *Advances in Chemistry Series, Biochemistry, Environmental Science and Technology, I&EC Fundamentals, I&EC Process Design and Development, I&EC Product Research and Development,* the *Journal of Agricultural and Food Chemistry,* and the *Journal of Chemical Documentation:*

Doe, A. B. (1962), Textbook of Chemistry, New York, N. Y., Jones, p 123.

(9) A. B. Smith, J. S. Doe, and P. Roe, "Textbook of Organic Chemistry," Vol. I, D. C. Jones and Co., New York, N. Y., 1961, pp 118-127.

(10) J. A. Jones, Ed., "Chelate Chemistry," 2nd ed, D. C. Jones and Co., New York, N. Y., 1964, pp 18-25.

(11) A. B. Doe, "Vacuum Techniques," Advances in Chemistry Series, No. 618, American Chemical Society, Washington, D. C., 1965, pp 110-115.

For instances in which reference is not to the author or editor of a whole book, but to a contributor to a part of it, the reference should be written as follows:

(12) A. B. Smith in "Fluorine Chemistry," 4th ed, J. S. Doe, Ed., D. C. Jones and Co., New York, N. Y., 1964, Chapter 7.

In *Advances in Chemistry Series, Biochemistry, Environmental Science and Technology, I&EC Fundamentals, I&EC Process Design and Development, I&EC Product Research and Development,* the *Journal of Agricultural and Food Chemistry,* and the *Journal of Chemical Documentation:*

Smith, A. B. (1964), in Fluorine Chemistry, Doe, J. S., Ed., New York, N. Y., Jones, Chapter 7.

REFERENCES TO SPECIAL MATERIALS

Theses—

(13) L. A. Doe, Ph. D. Thesis, The State University, New York, N. Y., 1962.

74

Government Bulletins—

(14) "Selected Values of Chemical Thermodynamic Properties," National Bureau of Standards Circular 500, U. S. Government Printing Office, Washington, D. C., 1950.

Reports—

(15) L. Roe and J. R. Doe, AEC Report 66-170, Los Altos, Calif., Feb 1964.

Patents—

(16) A. B. Doe, U. S. Patent 2542356 (1952).

(17) R. Roe, U. S. Patent 3000000 (1960); Chem. Abstr., 51, 2870 (1961).

(18) A. B. Doe, British Patent 1034050 (1966).

Abstracts of Meeting Papers—

(19) N. Roe and D. Doe, Abstracts, 150th National Meeting of the American Chemical Society, Atlantic City, N. J., Sept 1965, p 17C.

(20) N. Doe, Abstracts, 152nd National Meeting of the American Chemical Society, New York, N. Y., Sept 1966, No. U74.

REFERENCES TO UNPUBLISHED MATERIALS

For material presented before a society or other organization, but not published, use the following form:

(21) A. B. Roe, presented in part at the XXth Congress of the International Union of Chemistry, Paris, Sept 1960.

For material *accepted* for publication, but not yet published, use the following form:

(22) A. B. Roe, Spectrochim. Acta, in press.

Volume number, page number, and year should be added if they are available by the time the author receives the galley proofs.

For material *submitted* for publication, but not yet accepted, use the following form:

(23) A. B. Roe, submitted for publication in Spectrochim. Acta.

For *personal communications,* name of the writer, affiliation, and date should be given:

(24) C. D. Doe, The State University, personal communication, 1963.

In citation of personal communications the author should obtain permission from the person to be quoted.

In *Advances in Chemistry Series, Biochemistry, Environmental Science* and Technology, *I&EC Fundamentals, I&EC Process Design and Development, I&EC Product Research and Development,* the *Journal of Agricultural and Food Chemistry,* and the *Journal of Chemical Documentation,* unpublished work (unless already *accepted* for publication) and personal communications should not be included in the list of references but may be cited within the text as follows:

(A. B. Roe and G. Doe, 1962, unpublished data);

(A. B. Roe, 1963, personal communication).

SUBMISSION OF FINAL COPY

Manuscripts submitted to the journals must be in a form suitable for publication. In general the editorial staff does not make extensive changes. Manuscripts that do not follow the journals' conventions and requirements may be returned to the authors with a request that the authors revise them to conform with accepted style and practice.

TYPING Manuscripts must be typewritten double-spaced, on one side only, on 22 × 28 cm (8.5 × 11 in.), heavy-duty, white bond paper. *The original and two duplicates should be submitted.** A set of illustrations must accompany each copy. Clear, sharp copies made by a permanent duplication process are acceptable and are preferred for second and third copies to carbon copies.

Double space *all* copy: references, footnotes, tables, abstract, and figure captions as well as regular text. A liberal margin, at least 4 cm (1.5 in.), should be left on all sides of each page. Whenever possible, avoid dividing a word at the end of a line.

For instructions on preparing various portions of the manuscript, see the recommendations in sections II and III of this handbook. Additional hints to the typist are included in Appendix 4.

The final copy should be as nearly letter-perfect as possible. If a correction must be made, cross out the error and type the correct version *above* it. The use of Correction Tape or correction fluid (Snopake) to obliterate some errors is also recommended. Overtyping an incorrect letter with a correct letter gives the printer no indication of which letter to print. Do not type on margins or below the lines, or attach slips of paper to the pages. Retype any page needing lengthy insertions. Extensive handwritten revisions are not acceptable.

ARRANGEMENT The title page should include the title, by-line, author's affiliation, and abstract. All pages of a manuscript should be numbered consecutively, including the title page and list of footnotes and/or references. Page numbers should appear at top right. If a page is inserted or removed after the final copy has been prepared, succeeding page numbers must be altered accordingly. Figures and captions should be placed at the end of the paper. The captions should be grouped on one or more separate pages.

MAILING All manuscripts should be sent by first-class mail to the editor at the address given on the masthead of the appropriate journal. Illustrations in-

---

*Four manuscript copies are required for *Analytical Chemistry.*

cluding glossy prints and photographs should be adequately protected with cardboard.

A brief letter of transmittal should accompany each manuscript. The letter should contain a clear statement of intent that the manuscript be considered for publication, the name of the author, the title of the manuscript, and the complete address (the zip code must be included in U. S. addresses) to which the proofs (see p 82) should be sent. Membership in the American Chemical Society is *not* a prerequisite for publication in its journals. In general it is not necessary to include explanatory notes telling why that specific journal was chosen or discussing the manuscript. Submission of a manuscript to one of the Society journals implies that the same work is not under consideration for publication elsewhere, and that, if accepted, it will not be published elsewhere without the consent of the Society (see also Liability and Copying Rights, p 86).

Each manuscript will be acknowledged within a reasonable time.

IV.

The Editorial Process

Quantum yields of isomerization of 1, in cyclohexane, are summarized in Table I. Generally similar results were obtained, using benzene as the solvent. Over a 20-fold range the yield is independent of the concentration of the reactant. The apparent dependence on temperature is of doubtful significance but, if real, corresponds to an energy of activation of about 400 cal/mole. Oxygen has a small but definite inhibiting effect. This effect cannot be explained as due to peroxide formation, since its occurrence would increase the apparent quantum yield of dimerization.

Table I. Quantum Yields of Isomerization of 1,2-Bis(9-anthryl)ethane[a]

[A], M	[O$_2$], M	Temp, °C	φ
5.0×10^{-2}	2.0×10^{-4}	25	0.18
1.0×10^{-5}	2.0×10^{-4}	25	0.18
2.0×10^{-5}	2.0×10^{-4}	25	0.21
6.0×10^{-5}	2.0×10^{-4}	25	0.19
1.0×10^{-4}	2.0×10^{-4}	25	0.19
1.0×10^{-4}	2.0×10^{-4}	10	0.18
1.0×10^{-4}	2.0×10^{-4}	35	0.19
1.0×10^{-4}	2.0×10^{-4}	70	0.21
1.0×10^{-4}	$<10^{-6}$	25	0.26
1.0×10^{-4}	1.0×10^{-3}	25	0.17

[a] Solvent, cyclohexane; λ 365 mμ.

Quantum yields for the back reaction, which are listed in Table II, were calculated from the steady-state compositions; they depend on the measured values of the extinction coefficients, the quantum yield of the forward reaction, and the assumption that this yield is the same for 365 and 254 mμ. Light of 254 mμ was used to produce the steady state. Effects of the reactant concentration, oxygen, and temperature are similar to those observed for the forward reaction.

Table II. Steady-State Composition and Quantum Yields of the Reverse Isomerization[a]

[A]^0, M	[O$_2$], M	Temp, °C	Steady-state mole % of I	Quantum yield
1.0×10^{-6}	2.0×10^{-4}	25	4.5	0.42
5.0×10^{-6}	2.0×10^{-4}	25	4.1	0.37
1.0×10^{-5}	2.0×10^{-4}	25	4.5	0.41
1.0×10^{-5}	2.0×10^{-4}	10	4.8	0.44
1.0×10^{-5}	2.0×10^{-4}	35	4.8	0.45
1.0×10^{-5}	2.0×10^{-4}	70	5.3	0.49
1.0×10^{-5}	$<10^{-6}$	25	5.4	0.51

[a] Solvent, cyclohexane; λ 254 mμ.

Discussion

The observation that the quantum yield of isomerization is not affected by a 20-fold change in the concentration of the reactant indicates that the reaction is a

The manuscript page illustrated on pages 10, 16, and 28, set on galley proofs ready for the printer.

MANUSCRIPTS ARE JUDGED ON THE BASIS OF SIGNIFICANCE, originality, and clarity of presentation. The decision regarding acceptance or rejection of a manuscript is the prerogative of the particular editor; it is based in part on opinions solicited from authorities who serve as reviewers.

MANUSCRIPT REVIEW

Reviewers are selected in recognition of authoritative work in a specific field. The reviewer's duties are to assist in maintaining a high quality of scientific research reporting in the journals and to aid his colleagues by constructive criticism of their efforts. His report is specifically for the guidance of the editor, who usually transmits to the author the comments that will help in making any suggested revisions or in understanding the decision to accept or reject the paper. In most instances, the editor transmits the reviewer's report verbatim. The reviewer's comments usually are passed on anonymously. The reviewer may sometimes be identified where useful, but only with his permission.

A manuscript is the confidential property of the author and must not be reproduced or cited prior to publication without his permission. Reviewers must treat manuscripts under review as private communications and, if for any reason the prospective reviewer feels he cannot undertake the task without conflict, he should disqualify himself and promptly return the manuscript.

If a reviewer does not feel that he is scientifically qualified to review a manuscript he should return it to the editor. The reviewer may in some instances feel competent to review only a portion of a manuscript; even such limited review is usually preferred to return of the manuscript without review. A statement that he does not feel qualified to review a certain section of it then should be included in his report. The reviewer may wish, and indeed he is urged, to suggest names of specific persons who might be able to comment more appropriately on certain aspects of the manuscript.

Frequently the work described in a manuscript is deemed worthy of publication but is not acceptable in its submitted form. Such manuscripts are returned to the authors with suggestions for revision or inclusion of additional information. The author is not required to follow all suggestions made by reviewers but he should state to the editor his reasons for not following certain recommendations. The revised manuscript should be submitted in duplicate or, if requested, in triplicate. Lengthy handwritten additions by the authors are not acceptable. Complete retyping of the pages affected by extensive revision is required. Occasionally the revised manuscript will be reviewed again before a decision is reached regarding its publication.

In some cases, the editor of the journal to which a manuscript is submitted may feel that the paper would be more suitable for another journal. The manuscript then is returned with a suggestion that it be submitted elsewhere. If reviewers' reports also have been returned to the author, processing by another journal may be expedited by revision of the manuscript and submission of the revised version accompanied by the reviewers' reports and a covering letter outlining the changes which have been made.

PROCESSING OF ACCEPTED MANUSCRIPTS

All accepted manuscripts go directly from the editor to the technical editing office where they are prepared for the printer. The person submitting the manuscripts is notified of acceptance by the editor.

TECHNICAL EDITING The technical editor and his staff give instructions to the printer and mark the copy on matters of journal style, preparation of layout, selection of type, etc. Although he assumes no responsibility for accuracy of the author's data, clarity of his statements, or literary style, he may occasionally request certain additions, deletions, or clarification of copy.

The technical editor also prepares the page makeup of the journals, arranges all components of the composition in proper sequence and position, solves space or makeup problems well in advance of press time, and prepares tables of contents and indexes.

SYMBOLS AVAILABLE IN TYPE The printer has available a large selection of special characters and symbols in the various sizes of type required by the journals.* The use of unusual symbols must be avoided unless absolutely necessary.

The *Journal of Chemical and Engineering Data* and the *Journal of Chemical Documentation* are published by photocomposition instead of the usual typesetting process. For these journals the cost of providing additional characters is substantial; therefore special, unusual symbols will not be made available on an individual basis.

AUTHOR'S PROOF The senior author receives a copy of his manuscript set in type—a galley proof—for final approval before publication. A manuscript cannot be released for printing until the author's proof has been returned. Hence, proof should be checked and mailed back promptly according to individual journal instructions. To save time and reduce expense, foreign contributors may authorize a colleague in the United States to correct galley proofs.

---

*A list of these characters and symbols will be sent to interested authors upon request. Write to: American Chemical Society Publications, Research Journals Production Office, 20th and Northampton Streets, Easton, Pa. 18042.

When checking proofs, read thoroughly, and at least two times, one of which should be done *versus* the manuscript. Make only necessary corrections. Extensive changes may require editorial approval, require a new date of receipt, and delay publication. Printer's errors are corrected at no cost to the authors, but authors may be charged the cost of extensive resetting of lines made necessary by their own alterations. Data obtained after original submission of the manuscript should not be added to the text but may be attached to the galley proofs. A copy of the new information must be forwarded to the editor with an explanatory note. Where the desirability or necessity for the inclusion of such material can be demonstrated to the satisfaction of the editors, it will be inserted as *Notes Added in Proof*.

In marking the galley proofs the following points should be observed:

(1) Check all text, data, references against the original manuscript.

(2) Mark corrections in the margins in *pencil* (ink is used by editors and printers).

(3) Do not erase or in any way wholly obliterate type in the text. Instead, strike one line through the copy to be deleted and extend to the margin.

(4) Pay particular attention to equations, formulas, tables, captions, spelling of proper names, and numbering of illustrations, tables, and references.

(5) Clarify complicated corrections by rewriting the entire phrase or sentence in the margin, and encircle to indicate to the compositor that it is not an addition.

(6) Answer explicitly all queries.

PROOFREADER'S
MARKS

Every correction must be indicated in the margin; therefore each one requires two marks, one within the printed material and one in the margin. The one within the printed page is usually a caret or a line indicating where the correction is to be made. Marks to be used in correcting proofs are listed below.

Mark in Margin	Mark in Proof	Meaning
Size and style of type *wf* α/ *c*/	In the a-helical conformation	Wrong font (size *or* style of type)
lc	The X-Ray diffraction	Set in lower case
caps	Fractionation on dowex 50 columns	Set in capitals
sc	An addition of 4 g of DL-α-chloropropionic	Set in small caps
ital	The ortho to para rate ratios	Set in italic (or oblique) type
rom	The penta and hexaacetates	Set in Roman (or regular) type
bf	J.Amer.Chem.Soc., 77, 4048	Set in boldface type
✓	Near 3500 cm^{-1}	Superior letter or figure
ₐ	Calculation of the pK_a	Inferior letter or figure

Category	Symbol	Example	Meaning
Position	⌉	Calcd ⌉ for $C_8H_{18}O_6$	Move to right
	⌊	The solution ⌊was washed	Move to left
	⊔	Per mole of compound	Lower (letters or words)
	⊓	Under reduced pressure	Elevate (letters or words)
	=	identified during subsequent	Straighten line
	‖	All illustrations should in order of first appearance etc. Do not use terms such	Align type
	tr	Arabic with numerals,	Transpose
Spacing	⌒	for the mono hydrate	Close up entirely; take out space
	#	An amount of 1.8g	Insert space (or more space)
	⌄⌄⌄	Reflux for 3 hr	Even space
Insertion and deletion	℘	Mixture of glacial and acetic	Take out
	℘	Paper chromnatography	Take out and close up
	boiling/	In a water bath	Insert at this point
	stet	The dried (magnesium	Let it stand
Paragraphing	¶	¶A table may contain short d formulas should be avoided.	Begin a paragraph
	no ¶	of publishing an article. Industry, government, and	No paragraph
Punctuation	⊙	should be used Figures and	Period
	⋏ or ,/	were used camera diameter,	Comma
	⊙ or :/	payable to Chief, Photo	Colon
	⋏ or ;/	column width structures are	Semicolon
	⋎	Organic Division Committee	Apostrophe or 'single quote'
	⋎⋎	"Rules of Nomenclature, by	Quotation marks
	!/	his research Authors are	Exclamation point
	/=/	with two 100 ml portions	Hyphen
	slant line/	by plotting log K against 1 T	Insert solidus
	(/)	of 5-3-nitrophenyl compounds	Parentheses
	[/]	Brown[2] reports α^{25}D$+33°$	Brackets
Miscellaneous	h/⊘ o/⊘	articles elsewhere also must	Replace broken type
	⊘	without written permission	Reverse (upsidedown type
	e/	equivalant credit toward a	Correct letter marked

The Cr²⁺ Reductions.—The technique used in these reactions was like that previously described.[1] All reactions producing products were carried out at reduced pressure (60 mm) and gas evolution was measured manometrically. The products were identified by gas chromatography on a 30-ft Dimethylsulfolane column and by their infrared spectrum. When several products were produced, their concentrations were determined by integrating the gas chromatographic peaks. All reactions producing liquid or solid products were carried out under a positive pressure of nitrogen. The products were isolated and identified as described. All reactions were run at ~~the same~~ room temperature. Meso-2,3-Dibromobutane (1.7352 g, 0.00804 mole) in 50 ml of dmf was treated with 50 ml of 0.502 M Cr²⁺ (0.0251 mole). After several hours, 0.0140 mole of Cr²⁺ was consumed and 0.00691 mole of 2-butene (76% trans, 24% cis) was produced. Under the reaction conditions, neither trans- nor cis-2-butane was isomerized after exposure for 1 day.

CORRECTIONS Corrections for a paper that has already been published should be sent in duplicate to the editor of the journal. The following journals publish all corrections for the year in the last issue to appear in that year: *Accounts of Chemical Research, Chemical Reviews, Inorganic Chemistry,* the *Journal of Chemical Documentation,* the *Journal of Medicinal Chemistry, The Journal of Organic Chemistry, The Journal of Physical Chemistry.* The other journals publish corrections soon after they have been received.

REPRINTS

If reprints are desired, they should be ordered when the galley proofs are returned. The order form which is included with the galley proofs should be completed and returned as directed thereon.

PAGE CHARGE A form for the certification of page charge is also enclosed with the galley proofs for the following journals: *Biochemistry, Inorganic Chemistry,* the *Journal of the American Chemical Society,* the *Journal of Chemical Documentation,* the *Journal of Chemical and Engineering Data,* the *Journal of Medicinal Chemistry, The Journal of Organic Chemistry,* and *The Journal of Physical Chemistry.* The page charge is a publication service charge designed to cover some of the costs of publishing an article. Industry, government, and university administrators generally accept the page charge as a research expense, and funds are usually made available by the author's employer or by the sponsor of his research. *Authors are not expected to pay these charges personally.* Payment is not a condition for publication; editors and reviewers have no knowledge as to who has paid since bills are sent only after publication. If the page charge is honored, 100 free reprints, or the equivalent credit toward a larger purchase, are made available.

LIABILITY AND COPYING RIGHTS

Authors are solely responsible for the factual accuracy of their contributions. The Society and the Editors assume no responsibility for the statements and opinions advanced by the contributors to these publications.

Contributions that have appeared or have been accepted for publication with essentially the same content in another journal or in some freely available printed work (*e.g.,* government publications, proceedings) will not be published in the Society journals. This restriction does not apply to results previously published as *communications to the editor* in the same or other journals.

The Society owns the copyright for any paper that it publishes. Manuscripts accepted for publication in one of the journals of the Society may not be reprinted elsewhere without written permission from both the Society and the author; authors who wish to reproduce their articles elsewhere also must have the consent of the Society. Permission to quote portions of a paper will be granted provided that credit is given to the source.

Reproduction from the journals will be permitted only after obtaining the written consent of the Society. Requests should be addressed to the Publication Manager, Journals, in Washington, D. C.

The Society does not require a request for release of papers presented at its national or other meetings. Authors are free to submit these papers for publication to whatever journal they desire.

Correspondence regarding reprints, page charges, copyrights, and any request for additional information on the Society journals should be sent to American Chemical Society Publications, American Chemical Society, 1155 Sixteenth Street, N.W., Washington, D. C. 20036.

Appendix

Typographer correcting a galley of type, a time-consuming and expensive procedure.

Appendix 1

THE FOLLOWING COMMENTS on statistical evaluation of data have been prepared by Dr. W. J. Youden, who for many years has been statistical consultant with the National Bureau of Standards, where his major interest was the design and interpretation of experiments. A chemist as well as a recognized expert in the field of statistical design, Doctor Youden has numerous publications in the fields of applied statistics; he is author of the book "Statistical Methods for Chemists."

GUIDE TO EVALUATION OF DATA

At one time research papers included the experimental data in great detail. Statistical evaluation was relatively rare, but the detailed data made it possible for anyone interested to make his own analysis. Space limitations now place severe restrictions on the presentation of raw data. Averages and graphs replace the tabulation of individual observation. Therefore, it is incumbent on the author to provide the reader with some measure of the reliability of the reported averages.

Some appear to rely on using the number of 'significant' figures recorded in the average as an indication of the accuracy of the result. The number of figures is an extremely crude indication because one more (or one less) figure is a whole order of magnitude. Furthermore, any given average usually has two quite different uncertainties. Thus, if the item of interest is the *change* produced in the yields of a reaction by a change in temperature, this *difference* in yields is known comparatively accurately. If a systematic error is present, this error drops out of the difference. On the other hand, if one of these yields is reported as that to be expected from following a given procedure, the absolute value will almost certainly have a considerably larger error than that associated with the comparison of two or more yields.

The above distinction should always be kept in mind. Changes in a melting point as a result of further purification of a product are relatively easy to establish. Often the absolute value is important as an identification constant. Merely repeating the temperature measurements does not solve the difficulty. The absence of an appreciable systematic error must be established by checking out the melting point procedure on a compound with a known melting point in the neighborhood of the unknown.

The agreement of duplicate measurements reveals the *precision*. The standard deviation is the accepted unit for measuring the precision. The deviations of the individual results from their average are squared. The sum of the squares (numerator), after dividing by one less than the number of measurements (denominator), gives the square of the standard deviation and is called the *variance*. Seldom is one series of duplicate measurement sufficiently large to give a good estimate of the standard deviation. Several series believed to be comparable are combined by adding up the numerators and dividing by the sum of the denominators. The standard deviation so calculated refers to the *random* error in a single result. The standard deviation of the average N results (often called the *standard error*) is obtained by a further division by N. Such standard deviations are a guide to the number of places to be retained in an average, and should be reported along with the average.

Much confusion can be avoided if the author shows what formulas he uses, and an explicit reference to his source. If in doubt, do seek out a statistician because it is a pity to leave needless doubt in the mind of the reader who may have no means, from the material in the paper, to evaluate the reliability of the claims. In an era of compilations of scientific data, the importance of making it possible for the compilers to do their work properly should be obvious to all authors. Today there are chemical encyclopedias, treatises, and handbooks with brief expositions on statistical techniques for chemical data. There are also several substantial texts; a few are listed on p 117.

Appendix 2

THE INTERNATIONAL SYSTEM OF UNITS

The International System of Units as already mentioned was adopted by the eleventh General Conference on Weights and Measures in 1960 and endorsed by the International Organization for Standardization. The abbreviation for this system is SI in all languages.

In addition to having the obvious advantage of offering a real prospect of uniformity, the SI will be found superior to any other in current use, because it is a completely "coherent" system. In such a system the product or quotient of any two unit quantities leads to a unit of the resultant quantity; no numerical factors are involved, and there is only one unit for each type of quantity. The system can be extended without difficulty to provide the units required for all branches of science, so that everyone can speak the same "language." For example, the analogies between different processes are no longer obscured by the use of different units.

The SI is based on seven basic units. The names and symbols for the basic SI units, together with two supplementary units that have been officially adopted, are listed in Table I. The definitions of these basic units are given below. From these units all others are derived, and Table II includes most of those likely to be needed for papers published in the American Chemical Society journals. For convenience, special names and symbols have been agreed upon for some of the more important derived units, and these names can be used in forming further derived units. Nevertheless, all derived units can be expressed, if desired, in terms of the basic units.

Table I. Basic and Supplementary SI Units

Quantity	Name of unit	Unit symbol
length	metre	m
mass	kilogramme	kg
time	second	s
electric current	ampere	A
thermodynamic temperature	degree Kelvin	°K
luminous intensity	candela	cd
amount of substance	mole	mol
plane angle	radian	rad
solid angle	steradian	sr

DEFINITIONS OF THE BASIC SI UNITS

Metre:* The metre is the length equal to 1650763.73 (exactly) wavelengths under vacuum of the radiation corresponding to the transition between the energy levels $2p_{10}$ and $5d_5$ of the pure nuclide ^{86}Kr.

Kilogramme:* The kilogramme is the mass of the International Prototype Kilogramme which is in the custody of the Bureau International des Poids et Mesures at Sèvres, France.

Second: The second is still formally defined as the fraction 1/31556-925.9747 (exactly) of the tropical year for 1900 January 0 at 12 h ephemeris time. In October 1964, however, the twelfth Conférence Générale des Poids et Mesures recommended change to a unit based on an atomic radiation frequency and designated for temporary use the value 9192631-770 s^{-1} (exactly) for the frequency of the transition when undisturbed by external fields between the hyperfine levels $F = 4$, $M_F = 0$ and $F = 3$, $M_F = 0$ of the fundamental state $^2S_{\frac{1}{2}}$ of an atom of the pure nuclide ^{133}Cs. (This definition may be modified at the 1968 Conférence Générale.)

Ampere: The ampere is that constant current which, if maintained in two parallel rectilinear conductors, of infinite length and of negligible circular cross-section, at a distance apart of 1 metre under vacuum, would produce a force between the conductors equal to 2×10^{-7} newton per metre of length. (See Table II for dimensions of the newton.)

Degree Kelvin: The degree Kelvin is completely defined by the decision of the 1954 Conférence Générale to assign the value 273.16 degrees Kelvin (exactly) to the thermodynamic temperature at the triple point of water.

Candela: The candela, the unit of luminous intensity, is such that the luminance of a black body at the freezing point of platinum is 6×10^5 candelas per square metre.

*In the United States the spellings are meter and kilogram.

Mole: The mole is an amount of substance of a system which contains as many elementary units as there are carbon atoms in 0.012 kg (exactly) of the pure nuclide ^{12}C. The elementary unit must be specified and may be an atom, a molecule, an ion, an electron, a photon, etc., or a specified group of such entities.

Table II. Derived SI Units

Quantity	Name(s) of unit	Unit symbol or abbreviation, where differing from basic form	Unit expressed in terms of basic or supplementary units
area	square metre		m²
volume	cubic metre		m³
frequency	hertz, cycle per second†	Hz	s⁻¹
density	kilogramme per cubic metre		kg/m³
velocity	metre per second		m/s
angular velocity	radian per second		rad/s
acceleration	metre per second squared		m/s²
angular acceleration	radian per second squared		rad/s²
volumetric flow rate	cubic metre per second		m³/s
force	newton	N	kg m/s²
surface tension	newton per metre, joule per square metre	N/m, J/m²	kg/s²
pressure	newton per square metre, pascal†	N/m², Pa†	kg/m s²
viscosity, dynamic	newton-second per square metre, poiseuille†	N s/m², Pl†	kg/m s
viscosity, kinematic	metre squared per second		m²/s
work, torque, energy, quantity of heat	joule, newton-metre, watt-second	J, N m, W s	kg m²/s²
power, heat flux	watt, joule per second	W, J/s	kg m²/s³
heat flux density	watt per square metre	W/m²	kg/s³
volumetric heat release rate	watt per cubic metre	W/m³	kg/m s³
heat transfer coefficient	watt per square metre degree	W/m² deg	kg/s³ deg
heat capacity (specific)	joule per kilogramme degree	J/kg deg	m²/s² deg
capacity rate	watt per degree	W/deg	kg m²/s³ deg
thermal conductivity	watt per metre degree	W/m deg, $\dfrac{\text{Jm}}{\text{s m}^2\text{ deg}}$	kg m/s³ deg
quantity of electricity	coulomb	C	A s
electromotive force	volt	V, W/A	kg m²/A s³
electric field strength	volt per metre		V/m
electric resistance	ohm	Ω, V/A	kg m²/A² s³
electric conductivity	ampere per volt metre	A/V m	A² s³/kg m³
electric capacitance	farad	F, A s/V	A³ s⁴/kg m²
magnetic flux	weber	Wb, V s	kg m²/A s²
inductance	henry	H, V s/A	kg m²/A² s²
magnetic permeability	henry per metre	H/m	kg m/A² s²
magnetic flux density	tesla, weber per square metre	T, Wb/m²	kg/A s²
magnetic field strength	ampere per metre		A/m
magnetomotive force	ampere		A
luminous flux	lumen	lm	cd sr
luminance	candela per square metre		cd/m²
illumination	lux, lumen per square metre	lx, lm/m²	cd sr/m²

†Not used in all countries.

The criticism is frequently made that some of the SI units are of inconvenient size. The prefixes listed in Table III may be used to indicate decimal fractions or multiples of the basic or derived units.

There are a number of familiar units which differ from corresponding SI units only by powers of 10; some of these are mentioned in Table IV, but their use is to be progressively discouraged. Table V lists some units that, although not part of the SI, are expressed exactly in terms of the SI units. Their use also is to be progressively discouraged.

"International" electrical units. These units are obsolete having been replaced by the "absolute" (SI) units in 1948. The conversion factors which should be used with electrical measurements quoted in "international" units depend on where and on when the instruments used to make the measurements were calibrated. The following two sets of conversion factors refer, respectively, to the "mean international" units estimated by the ninth General Conference on Weights and Measures in 1948, and to the "U. S. international" units estimated by the U. S. National Bureau of Standards as applying to instruments calibrated by them prior to 1948.

1 "mean international ohm" $= 1.00049 \ \Omega$
1 "mean international volt" $= 1.00034 \ V$
1 "U. S. international ohm" $= 1.000495 \ \Omega$
1 "U. S. international volt" $= 1.000330 \ V$

Table III. Prefixes for SI Units

Fraction	Prefix	Symbol	Multiple	Prefix	Symbol
10^{-1}	deci	d	10	deka	da
10^{-2}	centi	c	10^2	hecto	h
10^{-3}	milli	m	10^3	kilo	k
10^{-6}	micro	μ	10^6	mega	M
10^{-9}	nano	n	10^9	giga	G
10^{-12}	pico	p	10^{12}	tera	T
10^{-15}	femto	f			
10^{-18}	atto	a			

Table IV. Decimal Fractions and Multiples of SI Units Having Special Names

Quantity	Name of unit	Unit symbol	Definition of unit
length	ångström	Å	10^{-10} m
length	micron [1]	μ	10^{-6} m
area	barn	b	10^{-28} m^2
volume	litre [2]	ℓ	10^{-3} m^3
mass	tonne	t	10^3 kg
force	dyne	dyn	10^{-5} N
pressure	bar	bar	10^{-5} N m^{-2}
energy	erg	erg	10^{-7} J
kinematic viscosity	stokes	St	10^{-4} m^2 s^{-1}
dynamic viscosity	poise	P	10^{-1} kg m^{-1} s^{-1}

(1) The name micron, symbol μ, is still used by some spectroscopists instead of its SI equivalent the micrometre, symbol μm, and the millimicron, symbol mμ, instead of the nanometre, symbol nm

(2) By decision of the twelfth Conférence Générale des Poids et Mesures in October 1964 the old definition of the litre (1.000028 dm^3) was rescinded. The word litre is now regarded as a special name for the cubic decimetre. Neither the word litre nor its symbol ℓ should be used to express results of high precision.
  In the United States the spelling is liter.

Table V. Other Units Defined in Terms of SI Units

The following list is by no means exhaustive. Each of the definitions given in the fourth column is *exact*.

Quantity	Name of unit	Unit symbol	Definition of unit
length	inch	in	2.54×10^{-2} m
mass	pound (avoirdupois)	lb	0.45359237 kg
force	kilogramme-force	kgf	9.80665 N
pressure	atmosphere	atm	101325 N m^{-2}
pressure	torr	Torr	(101325/760) N m^{-2}
pressure	conventional millimetre of mercury [1]	mmHg	$13.5951 \times 980.665 \times 10^{-2}$ N m^{-2}
energy	kilowatt-hour	kWh	3.6×10^{6} J
energy	thermochemical calorie	cal	4.184 J
energy	international steam table calorie	cal$_{IT}$	4.1868 J
thermodynamic temperature (T)	degree Rankine [2]	°R	(5/9) °K
customary temperature (t)	degree Celsius [2]	°C	$t/°C = T/°K - 273.15$
customary temperature (t)	degree Fahrenheit [2]	°F	$t/°F = T/°R - 459.67$
radioactivity	curie	Ci	3.7×10^{10} s^{-1}

The following units defined in terms of the best available experimental values of certain physical constants may be converted to SI units. The factors for conversion of these units are subject to change in the light of new experimental measurements of the constants involved.

Quantity	Name of unit	Unit symbol	Conversion factor
energy	electron-volt	eV	eV $\approx 1.6021 \times 10^{-19}$ J
mass	unified atomic mass unit	u	u $\approx 1.66041 \times 10^{-27}$ kg

(1) The conventional millimetre of mercury, symbol mmHg (not mm Hg), is the pressure exerted by a column exactly 1 mm high of a fluid of density exactly 13.5951 g cm^{-3} in a place where the gravitational acceleration is exactly 980.665 cm s^{-2}. The mmHg differs from the Torr by less than 2×10^{-7} Torr.

(2) The ° sign and the letter following form one symbol and there should be no space between them. Example: 25 °C not 25° C.

VALUES OF THE FUNDAMENTAL CONSTANTS FOR CHEMISTRY*

To ensure consistency in the communication of data, investigators should use the recommended values of the fundamental constants in reducing their data. The values presented here are those in NAS–NRC recommendations based on the 1963 report by J. W. M. DuMond and E. R. Cohen.** The constants have been classified arbitrarily in three categories:

*This section is based on the IUPAC 1964 recommendations by F. D. Rossini, "Values of the Fundamental Constants for Chemistry," Physical Chemistry Division, Commission on Thermodynamics and Thermochemistry, *Pure Appl. Chem.*, **9** (3), 453 (1964).

"New Values for the Physical Constants Recommended by NAS–NRC," *Nat. Bur. Stand. (U. S.) Tech. News Bull.*, **47 (10) (Oct 1963).

(1) the *defined* constants (see Table I), the values of which are fixed exactly by definition as approved by various international commissions;

(2) The *basic* constants (see Table II), the values of which are, in the main, obtained from experimental measurements in terms of the fundamental units of length, mass, and time; and

(3) the *derived* constants (see Table III), the values of which are, in the main, obtained from the foregoing two categories and appropriate physical relations.

Study of the values of the fundamental constants is continuing, so that revisions may be expected at suitable intervals.

Table I. Values of the "Defined" Constants

Constant	Symbol	Value (exact, by definition)
Unified atomic mass unit	u	1/12 times the mass of an atom of ^{12}C
Mole	mol	The amount of a substance, of specified chemical formula, containing the same number of formula units (molecules, atoms, ions, electrons, or other entities) as there are atoms in 12 g (exactly) of the pure nuclide ^{12}C
Standard acceleration of gravity, in free fall	g	980.665 cm s^{-2}
Normal atmosphere, pressure	atm	1013250 dyn cm^{-2}
Absolute temperature of the triple point of water†	T_{tp}	273.16 °K
Thermochemical calorie	cal	4.184 J
International steam calorie	cal$_{IT}$	4.1868 J
Inch	in	2.54 cm
Pound, avoirdupois	lb	453.59237 g

†The difference between the temperature of the triple point of water and the so-called "ice point" (temperature of equilibrium of solid and liquid water saturated with air at one atmosphere) is accurately known: T(triple point) $-$ T (ice point) = 0.0100 ± 0.0001 °K.

Table II. Recommended Values of the "Basic" Constants†

Constant	Symbol	Value (with estimated uncertainty)	
Velocity of light *in vacuo*	c	2.997925×10^{10} cm s^{-1} ±0.000003	
Avogadro number	N	6.02252×10^{23} ±0.00028	molecules mol^{-1}
Faraday constant	F	96487.0 ±1.6	coulomb equiv^{-1}
		23060.9 ±0.4	cal volt^{-1} equiv^{-1}
Planck constant	h	6.6256×10^{-27} ±0.0005	erg s
Pressure-volume product for one mole of gas at 0°C and zero pressure	$(PV)^{P=0}_{0°C}$	2271.06 ±0.12	J mol^{-1}
		22413.6 ±1.2	cm^3 atm mol^{-1}

†The selection of these constants as the five "basic" ones is somewhat arbitrary. A least squares adjustment such as that of Cohen and DuMond actually treats, on an equal basis, both the "basic" constant and those "derived" constants which can be evaluated experimentally. In order to evaluate the accuracy of any constant derived from those on this list it is necessary to use the complete error matrix as more fully explained in the report of Cohen and DuMond.

Table III. Recommended Values of the "Derived" Constants*

Constant	Symbol and relation	Value (with estimated uncertainty)	
Elementary charge	$e = F/N$	4.80298×10^{-10}	cm$^{3/2}$ g$^{1/2}$ s^{-1} (esu)
		± 0.00020	
Gas constant	$R = (PV)\,{}^{P=0}_{0°C}/T_{0°C}$	8.31433	J deg^{-1} mol^{-1}
		± 0.00044	
		1.98717	cal deg^{-1} mol^{-1}
		± 0.00011	
Boltzmann constant	$k = R/N$	1.38054×10^{-16}	erg deg^{-1}
		± 0.00009	molecule^{-1}
Second radiation constant	$c_2 = hc/k$	1.43879	cm deg
		± 0.00009	
Einstein constant relating mass and energy	$Y = c^2$	8.987554×10^{13} J g^{-1}	
		± 0.000018	
		2.148076×10^{13} cal g^{-1}	
		± 0.000004	
Constant relating wavenumber and energy	$Z = Nhc$	11.96255	J cm mol^{-1}
		± 0.00038	
		2.85912	cal cm mol^{-1}
		± 0.00009	

*Ref ** page 94 gives values for additional "derived" constants.

CONVERSION FACTORS

Reproduced from "Selected Values of Properties of Chemical Compounds," Thermodynamics Research Center, Texas A&M University, College Station, Texas.

To convert the numerical value of a property expressed in one of the units in the left-hand column of a table to the numerical value of the same property in one of the units in the top row of the same table, multiply the former value by the factor in the block common to both units. The factors have been carried out to seven significant figures, as derived from the constants discussed on the previous pages and the definitions of the units. However, this does not mean that the factors are always known to that accuracy. Numbers followed by . . . are to be continued indefinitely with repetition of the same pattern of digits. Factors written with fewer than seven significant digits should be taken as exact values. Numbers followed by an asterisk (*) are definitions of the relation between the two units.

THE MOL UNIT

Units		g-mol (Unified)	g-mol (Chemists')	g-mol (Physicists')	lb-mol (Unified)	lb-mol (Chemists')	lb-mol (Physicists')
1 g-mol (Unified)	=	1	1.000043	1.000318	2.204623×10^{-3}	2.204717×10^{-3}	2.2053237×10^{-3}
1 g-mol (Chemists')	=	0.9999570	1	1.000275	2.204528×10^{-3}	2.204623×10^{-3}	2.205229×10^{-3}
1 g-mol (Physicists')	=	0.9996821	0.999725	1	2.203922×10^{-3}	2.204017×10^{-3}	2.204623×10^{-4}
1 lb-mol (Unified)	=	453.5924	453.6119	453.7366	1	1.000043	1.000318
1 lb-mol (Chemists')	=	453.5729	453.5924	453.7171	0.9999570	1	1.000275
1 lb-mol (Physicists')	=	453.4482	453.4677	453.5924	0.9996821	0.999725	1

UNITS OF LENGTH

Units		cm	m	in.	ft	yd	mile
1 cm	=	1	0.01*	0.3937008	0.03280840	0.01093613	6.213712×10^{-6}
1 m	=	100.	1	39.37008	3.280840	1.093613	6.213712×10^{-4}
1 in.	=	2.54*	0.0254	1	0.08333333...	0.02777777...	1.578283×10^{-5}
1 ft	=	30.48	0.3048	12.*	1	0.3333333...	$1.893939 \times 10^{-4}...$
1 yd	=	91.44	0.9144	36.	3.*	1	$5.681818 \times 10^{-4}...$
1 mile	=	1.609344×10^{5}	1.609344×10^{3}	6.336×10^{4}	5280.*	1760.	1

UNITS OF AREA

Units		cm²	m²	in.²	ft²	yd²	mile²
1 cm²	=	1	10^{-4}*	0.1550003	1.076391×10^{-3}	1.195990×10^{-4}	3.861022×10^{-11}
1 m²	=	10^{4}	1	1550.003	10.76391	1.195990	3.861022×10^{-7}
1 in.²	=	6.4516*	6.4516×10^{-4}	1	$6.944444 \times 10^{-3}...$	7.716049×10^{-4}	2.490977×10^{-10}
1 ft²	=	929.0304	0.09290304	144.*	1	0.1111111...	3.587007×10^{-8}
1 yd²	=	8361.273	0.8361273	1296.	9.*	1	3.228306×10^{-7}
1 mile²	=	2.589988×10^{10}	2.589988×10^{6}	4.014490×10^{9}	2.78784×10^{7}*	3.0976×10^{6}	1

UNITS OF VOLUME

Units		cm³	liter	in.³	ft³	qt	gal
1 cm³	=	1	10^{-3}	0.06102374	3.531467×10^{-5}	1.056688×10^{-3}	2.641721×10^{-4}
1 liter	=	1000.*	1	61.02374	0.03531467	1.056688	0.2641721
1 in.³	=	16.38706*	0.01638706	1	5.787037×10^{-4}	0.01731602	4.329004×10^{-3}
1 ft³	=	28316.85	28.31685	1728.*	1	2.992208	7.480520
1 qt	=	946.353	0.946353	57.75	0.0342014	1	0.25
1 gal (U. S.)	=	3785.412	3.785412	231.*	0.1336806	4.*	1

UNITS OF MASS

Units		g	kg	oz	lb	metric ton	ton
1 g	=	1	10^{-3}	0.03527396	2.204623×10^{-3}	10^{-6}	1.102311×10^{-6}
1 kg	=	1000.	1	35.27396	2.204623	10^{-3}	1.102311×10^{-3}
1 oz (avdp)	=	28.34952	0.02834952	1	0.0625	2.834952×10^{-5}	$5. \times 10^{-4}$
1 lb (avdp)	=	453.5924	0.4535924	16.*	1	4.535924×10^{-4}	0.0005
1 metric ton	=	10^{6}	1000.*	35273.96	2204.623	1	1.102311
1 ton	=	907184.7	907.1847	32000.	2000.*	0.9071847	1

UNITS OF DENSITY

Units		$g\ cm^{-3}$	$g\ l.^{-1}$	$oz\ in.^{-3}$	$lb\ in.^{-3}$	$lb\ ft^{-3}$	$lb\ gal^{-1}$
$1\ g\ cm^{-3}$	=	1	1000.	0.5780365	0.03612728	62.42795	8.345403
$1\ g\ l.^{-1}$	=	10^{-3}	1	5.780365×10^{-4}	3.612728×10^{-5}	0.06242795	8.345403×10^{-3}
$1\ oz\ in.^{-3}$	=	1.729994	1729.994	1	0.0625	108.	14.4375
$1\ lb\ in.^{-3}$	=	27.67991	27679.91	16.	1	1728.	231.
$1\ lb\ ft^{-3}$	=	0.01601847	16.01847	9.259259×10^{-3}	5.7870370×10^{-4}	1	0.1336806
$1\ lb\ gal^{-1}$	=	0.1198264	119.8264	4.749536×10^{-3}	4.3290043×10^{-3}	7.480519	1

UNITS OF PRESSURE

Units		$dyn\ cm^{-2}$	bar	atm	$kg\ (wt)\ cm^{-2}$	mmHg (torr)	in. Hg	$lb\ (wt)\ in.^{-2}$
$1\ dyn\ cm^{-2}$	=	1	10^{-6}	9.869233×10^{-7}	1.019716×10^{-6}	7.500617×10^{-4}	2.952999×10^{-5}	1.450377×10^{-5}
1 bar	=	10^{6*}	1	0.9869233	1.019716	750.0617	29.52999	14.50377
1 atm	=	1013250.*	1.013250	1	1.033227	760.	29.92126	14.69595
$1\ kg\ (wt)\ cm^{-2}$	=	980665.	0.980665	0.9678411	1	735.5592	28.95903	14.22334
1 mmHg (torr)	=	1333.224	1.333224×10^{-3}	1.3157895×10^{-3}	1.3595099×10^{-3}	1	0.03937008	0.01933678
1 in. Hg	=	33863.88	0.03386388	0.03342105	0.03453155	25.4	1	0.4911541
$1\ lb\ (wt)\ in.^{-2}$	=	68947.57	0.06894757	0.06804596	0.07030696	51.71493	2.036021	1

UNITS OF ENERGY*

Units		g mass (energy equiv)	J	int J	cal	cal_{IT}	Btu_{IT}	kW hr	hp hr	ft-lb (wt)	cu ft-lb (wt) in.$^{-2}$	l.-atm
1 g mass (energy equiv)	=	1	8.987554×10^{13}	8.986071×10^{13}	2.148077×10^{13}	2.146640×10^{13}	8.518558×10^{10}	2.496543×10^{7}	3.347919×10^{7}	6.628880×10^{13}	4.603399×10^{11}	8.870026×10^{11}
1 J	=	1.112650×10^{-14}	1	0.999835	0.2390057	0.2388459	9.478172×10^{-4}	$2.777777\ldots \times 10^{-7}$	3.725062	0.7375622	5.121960×10^{-3}	9.869233×10^{-3}
1 int J	=	1.112833×10^{-14}	1.000165	1	0.2390452	0.2388853	9.479735×10^{-4}	2.778236×10^{-7}	3.725676×10^{-7}	0.7376839	5.122805×10^{-3}	9.870862×10^{-3}
1 cal	=	4.655327×10^{-14}	4.184*	4.183310	1	0.9993312	3.965667×10^{-3}	$1.1622222\ldots \times 10^{-6}$	1.558562×10^{-6}	3.085960	2.143028×10^{-2}	0.04129287
1 cal_{IT}	=	4.658442×10^{-14}	4.1868*	4.186109	1.000669	1	3.968321×10^{-3}	1.163000×10^{-6}	1.559609×10^{-6}	3.088025	2.144462×10^{-2}	0.04132050
1 Btu_{IT}	=	1.173908×10^{-11}	1055.056	1054.882	252.1644	251.9958*	1	2.930711×10^{-4}	3.930148×10^{-4}	778.1693	5.403953	10.41259
1 kW hr	=	4.005539×10^{-8}	3600000.*	3599406.	860420.7	859845.2	3412.142	1	1.341022	2655224.	18439.06	35529.24
1 hp hr	=	2.986930×10^{-8}	2684519.	2684077.	641615.6	641186.5	2544.33	0.7456998	1	1980000.*	13750.	26494.15
1 ft-lb (wt)	=	1.508550×10^{-14}	1.355818	1.355594	0.3240483	0.3238315	1.285067×10^{-3}	3.766161×10^{-7}	$5.050505\ldots \times 10^{-7}$	1	$6.944444\ldots \times 10^{-3}$	0.01338088
1 cu ft-lb (wt) in.$^{-2}$	=	2.172313×10^{-12}	195.2378	195.2056	46.66295	46.63174	0.1850497	5.423272×10^{-5}	$7.272727\ldots \times 10^{-5}$	144.*	1	1.926847
1 l.-atm	=	1.127392×10^{-12}	101.3250	101.3083	24.21726	24.20106	0.09603757	2.814583×10^{-5}	3.774419×10^{-5}	74.73349	0.5189825	1

*The electrical units in these tables are those in terms of which certification of standard cells, standard resistances, etc., is made by the National Bureau of Standards. Unless otherwise indicated, all electrical units are absolute.

nits	erg molecule⁻¹	J mol⁻¹	int J mol⁻¹	cal mol⁻¹	eV molecule⁻¹	int eV molecule⁻¹	wavenumber (cm⁻¹)
rg molecule⁻¹ =	1	6.022520×10^{16}	6.021526×10^{16}	1.439417×10^{16}	6.241808×10^{11}	6.239748×10^{11}	5.034474×10^{15}
J mol⁻¹ =	1.660435×10^{-17}	1	0.9998350	0.2390057	1.036411×10^{-5}	1.036069×10^{-5}	8.359414×10^{-2}
int J mol⁻¹ =	1.660709×10^{-17}	1.000165	1	0.2390452	1.036582×10^{-5}	1.036240×10^{-5}	8.360793×10^{-2}
cal mol⁻¹ =	6.947258×10^{-17}	4.1840	4.18331	1	4.336345×10^{-5}	4.334914×10^{-5}	0.3497579
V molecule⁻¹ =	1.602100×10^{-12}	96486.79	96470.87	23060.90	1	0.9996701	8065.730
int eV olecule⁻¹ =	1.602393×10^{-12}	96518.63	96502.71	23068.51	1.000330	1	8068.392
wavenumber m⁻¹) =	1.986305×10^{-16}	11.96256	11.96059	2.859121	1.239813×10^{-4}	1.239404×10^{-4}	1

NITS OF SPECIFIC ENERGY*

Units		$J\ g^{-1}$	int $J\ g^{-1}$	cal g^{-1}	$cal_{IT}\ g^{-1}$	$Btu_{IT}\ lb^{-1}$	kW hr lb⁻¹
1 J g⁻¹	=	1	0.999835	0.2390057	0.2388459	0.4299226	1.259979×10^{-4}
1 int J g⁻¹	=	1.000165	1	0.2390452	0.2388853	0.4299936	1.260187×10^{-4}
1 cal g⁻¹	=	4.184*	4.18331	1	0.9993312	1.798796	5.271752×10^{-4}
1 cal$_{IT}$ g⁻¹	=	4.1868*	4.186109	1.000669	1	1.8*	5.275279×10^{-4}
1 Btu$_{IT}$ lb⁻¹	=	2.326000	2.325616	0.5559273	0.5555555...	1	2.390711×10^{-4}
1 kW hr lb⁻¹	=	7936.641	7935.332	1896.903	1895.643	3414.425	1

NITS OF SPECIFIC ENERGY PER DEGREE*

Units		$J\ g^{-1}\ °C^{-1}$	int $J\ g^{-1}\ °C^{-1}$	cal $g^{-1}\ °C^{-1}$	$cal_{IT}\ g^{-1}\ °C^{-1}$	$Btu_{IT}\ lb^{-1}\ °F^{-1}$	kW hr lb⁻¹ °F⁻¹
1 J g⁻¹ °C⁻¹	=	1	0.999835	0.2390057	0.2388459	0.2388459	6.999883×10^{-5}
1 int J g⁻¹ °C⁻¹	=	1.000165	1	0.2390452	0.2388853	0.2388853	7.001037×10^{-5}
1 cal g⁻¹ °C⁻¹	=	4.184*	4.183310	1	0.999312	0.9993312	2.928751×10^{-4}
1 cal$_{IT}$ g⁻¹ °C⁻¹	=	4.1868*	4.186109	1.000669	1	1*	2.930711×10^{-4}
1 Btu$_{IT}$ lb⁻¹ °F⁻¹	=	4.1868	4.186109	1.000669	1*	1	2.930711×10^{-4}
1 kW hr lb⁻¹ °F⁻¹	=	14285.95	14283.60	3414.425	3412.142	3412.142	1

TABLE OF RELATIVE ATOMIC WEIGHTS 1961*

Based on the Atomic Mass of $^{12}C=12$

The values for atomic weights given in the table apply to elements as they exist in nature, without artificial alteration of their isotopic composition, and, further, to natural mixtures that do not include isotopes of radiogenic origin.

Alphabetical Order

Name	Symbol	Atomic number	Atomic weight	Name	Symbol	Atomic number	Atomic weight
Actinium	Ac	89	....	Mercury	Hg	80	200.59
Aluminum	Al	13	26.9815	Molybdenum	Mo	42	95.94
Americium	Am	95	....	Neodymium	Nd	60	144.24
Antimony	Sb	51	121.75	Neon	Ne	10	20.183
Argon	Ar	18	39.948	Neptunium	Np	93	....
Arsenic	As	33	74.9216	Nickel	Ni	28	58.71
Astatine	At	85	....	Niobium	Nb	41	92.906
Barium	Ba	56	137.34	Nitrogen	N	7	14.0067
Berkelium	Bk	97	....	Nobelium	No	102	....
Beryllium	Be	4	9.0122	Osmium	Os	76	190.2
Bismuth	Bi	83	208.980	Oxygen	O	8	15.9994[a]
Boron	B	5	10.811[a]	Palladium	Pd	46	106.4
Bromine	Br	35	79.904[b]	Phosphorus	P	15	30.9738
Cadmium	Cd	48	112.40	Platinum	Pt	78	195.09
Calcium	Ca	20	40.08	Plutonium	Pu	94	....
Californium	Cf	98	....	Polonium	Po	84	....
Carbon	C	6	12.01115[a]	Potassium	K	19	39.102
Cerium	Ce	58	140.12	Praseodymium	Pr	59	140.907
Cesium	Cs	55	132.905	Promethium	Pm	61	....
Chlorine	Cl	17	35.453[b]	Protactinium	Pa	91	....
Chromium	Cr	24	51.996[b]	Radium	Ra	88	....
Cobalt	Co	27	58.9332	Radon	Rn	86	....
Copper	Cu	29	63.546[b]	Rhenium	Re	75	186.2
Curium	Cm	96	....	Rhodium	Rh	45	102.905
Dysprosium	Dy	66	162.50	Rubidium	Rb	37	85.47
Einsteinium	Es	99	....	Ruthenium	Ru	44	101.07
Erbium	Er	68	167.26	Samarium	Sm	62	150.35
Europium	Eu	63	151.96	Scandium	Sc	21	44.956
Fermium	Fm	100	....	Selenium	Se	34	78.96
Fluorine	F	9	18.9984	Silicon	Si	14	28.086[a]
Francium	Fr	87	....	Silver	Ag	47	107.868[b]
Gadolinium	Gd	64	157.25	Sodium	Na	11	22.9898
Gallium	Ga	31	69.72	Strontium	Sr	38	87.62
Germanium	Ge	32	72.59	Sulfur	S	16	32.064[a]
Gold	Au	79	196.967	Tantalum	Ta	73	180.948
Hafnium	Hf	72	178.49	Technetium	Tc	43	....
Helium	He	2	4.0026	Tellurium	Te	52	127.60
Holmium	Ho	67	164.930	Terbium	Tb	65	158.924
Hydrogen	H	1	1.00797[a]	Thallium	Tl	81	204.37
Indium	In	49	114.82	Thorium	Th	90	232.038
Iodine	I	53	126.9044	Thulium	Tm	69	168.934
Iridium	Ir	77	192.2	Tin	Sn	50	118.69
Iron	Fe	26	55.847[b]	Titanium	Ti	22	47.90
Krypton	Kr	36	83.80	Tungsten	W	74	183.85
Lanthanum	La	57	138.91	Uranium	U	92	238.03
Lead	Pb	82	207.19	Vanadium	V	23	50.942
Lithium	Li	3	6.939	Xenon	Xe	54	131.30
Lutetium	Lu	71	174.97	Ytterbium	Yb	70	173.04
Magnesium	Mg	12	24.312	Yttrium	Y	39	88.905
Manganese	Mn	25	54.9380	Zinc	Zn	30	65.37
Mendelevium	Md	101	....	Zirconium	Zr	40	91.22

[a]Atomic weights so designated are known to be variable because of natural variations in isotopic composition. The observed ranges are:

Hydrogen	±0.00001	Carbon	±0.00005	Silicon	±0.001
Boron	±0.003	Oxygen	±0.0001	Sulfur	±0.003

[b]Atomic weights so designated are believed to have the following experimental uncertainties:

Chlorine	±0.001	Copper	±0.001	Bromine	±0.001
Chromium	±0.001	Iron	±0.003	Silver	±0.001

*This table includes the revisions of the atomic weights for Bromine, Copper, and Silver as adopted by the International Commission on Atomic Weights at the IUPAC Conference, July 1965.

Appendix 4

HINTS TO THE TYPIST

Typewriters used in typing chemistry text and mathematics may be manual or electric. The style or model of typewriter is relatively unimportant. The flexibility of the standard typewriter keyboard may be increased by using the typewriter attachment called "Typit."

Typit can be used with any typewriter. Special letters and symbols are mounted individually on small plastic rods which are inserted into a holder fastened to the front paper scale. Then, any key that is struck causes this symbol to print on the copy. The "Typit" is quickly removed and typing is continued. A large variety of symbols are available—the Greek alphabet, brackets and braces, technical and scientific symbols, subscripts and super-scripts for numerals, symbols, Greek letters, and Latin upper case and lower case letters. Some Typit key bars especially useful for chemistry text are:

Symbols for organic equations ($\backslash\backslash$ $/\!/$ $/$ $\backslash$ —),

symbols for various arrows (← ⇆ → ↑ ↓ ⇅),

a degree sign (°), an umlaut (¨)

When the work is not to be reproduced in quantity* white bond paper should be used. Clear, sharp copies made by a permanent duplication process are acceptable for the primary copy and are preferred, for second and third copies, to carbon copies. If it is necessary to use carbon copies, a good quality (cockle-finish) onionskin paper should be used. A nylon or carbon ribbon in the typewriter is not as inky as a cotton ribbon and gives clearer impressions. For clean, accurate erasures on both original and carbon copies a soft eraser (*i.e.,* a Multilith eraser) should be used first to remove excess ink; then a stick eraser should be used. Correction tape may also be used for work done on bond paper.

All typing including abstract, footnotes, tables, etc., should be double-spaced. Margins should be approximately 4 cm. Footnotes are preferably typed together in order at the end of the manuscript, although they may be typed immediately following the line in which reference is made to them, separated from the text by a line above and below. Display material should be separated from the text by a triple-space below the lowest point. Because the styles of report presentation change, the manner in which items are arranged on the pages will differ for each journal. Illustrations and recommendations in Sections II and III of this Handbook should be carefully followed. All symbols, Greek letters, signs, large parentheses, braces, etc., for which you may not have typewriter keys must be traced

---

*For a large number of reproductions the clearest reproduced copy will be obtained from a Multilith master mat. A stencil is not good for chemical work since so many figures must be drawn and the stencil tears easily. The Ditto, Ozalid, Xerox, and similar processes can be satisfactorily employed.

on the copy. Templates should be used as guides in drawing.* When using bond paper and carbon copies clip sheets in two or three places to a file folder, place on a hard surface, and trace all drawings with a black ball-point pen. It is important to line up the sheets carefully both at the beginning and when returning them to the typewriter. In some cases it may be easier to plan the diagram, complete all typing, then add the drawings. In others you may prefer to draw the diagram first and then do the typing.

CHEMICAL SYMBOLS   Each chemical symbol representing an element is either one capital letter or one capital letter and one lower-case letter.

Do not add space between symbols and numbers in chemical formulas; they are typed *close* in this style:

$$C_2H_2O_4, \quad NaHSO_4, \quad Ca(HCO_3)_2$$

Add the usual space around the symbols for "plus," "equal," and "arrows" in chemical formulas.

CHEMICAL NOMENCLATURE   Take care in checking spelling, capitalizing, combining forms, spacing, underscoring for italics. Follow as closely as possible the style of the journal for which you are preparing the manuscript.

Position numbers precede the part of the name to which they refer and are connected to the name with hyphens. Separate two or more numbers with commas. Sometimes periods are used between bracketed numbers.

```
2,2-dichloropropane
2-amino-4,6-dichloropyrimidine
2,5-dichloro-2'-hydroxy-4-methylazobenzene
1-chlorobicyclo[2.2.2]octane
```

If a compound begins a sentence, type the first name only with an initial capital.

```
1-chloro-2-methyl-1-propene (within a sentence)
1-Chloro-2-methyl-1-propene (begins a sentence)
```

Letter abbreviations for specific prefixes and Greek letters may be combined with position numbers. Most letter abbreviations should be underscored to indicate italics. Greek letters should not be underlined.

```
4,5-dibromo-o-xylene
γ-aminopyridine
m-hydroxybenzaldehyde
```

SCRIPT PATTERNS   **Superscripts and Subscripts—** Superscripts, also referred to as superiors or exponents, and subscripts, often called inferiors, may be single letters, Greek letters, numbers, mathematical symbols, or groups (multiple scripts) which form complex patterns.

A super- or sub-pattern belongs specifically to a single character or to a pattern of many characters. This means that all of these script patterns are typed as close as possible to the character or pattern to which they belong, but superscripts and subscripts that belong to the same character should not be typed directly above one another.

---

*Recommended templates are: L. F. Fieser's Chemist's Triangle, Griffin Organic Stencil No. 890592, C-Thru Stencil No. 318, RapiDesign No. 83.

Single superscripts are typed slightly above the line character, and single subscripts slightly below the line character. To line up all superscripts and subscripts first type the main line leaving space for the superscripts and subscripts, then go back and type them in. There may be superscripts and subscripts *to* superscripts, and superscripts and subscripts *to* subscripts. Be careful that these extra scripts do not wander too far away from the pattern to which they belong.

$$3Ca^{2+} + 2PO_4{}^{3-} \rightarrow Ca_3(PO_4)_2$$

$$\underline{K}_{sp} = (\gamma_+ \underline{m}_+)^{\underline{a}}(\gamma_- \underline{m}_-)^{\underline{b}} = \underline{m}_+{}^{\underline{a}}\underline{m}_-{}^{\underline{b}}(\gamma_\pm)^{\underline{a}+\underline{b}}$$

$$\tilde{\underline{v}}^E = (\tilde{\underline{v}}^o)^{7/3}[4/3 - (\tilde{\underline{v}}^o)^{1/3}]^{-1}[\tilde{\underline{T}} - \tilde{\underline{T}}^o]$$

In typing *thermodynamic* symbols, such as $S^\circ{}_0$ and $H^\circ{}_0$, use the degree sign as superscript and zero as the subscript. Remember that the scripts should not be one above the other.

Fractional Scripts — Wherever possible fractions should be typed in a script pattern with the diagonal fraction bar instead of a horizontal fraction bar.

$$(2\underline{D}_{\underline{z}})^{1/2}; \quad \underline{xy}/\underline{z}$$

Subscript Zero — Do not use lower-case letter o in a subscript pattern as a substitute for the cipher zero (0). All typed subscripts must be uniform in size. The lower-case o may be used for the "degree" symbol $(^\circ K)$, but it is incorrect when used as either a subscript zero or a superscript zero. In some cases a note in the margin may be necessary to remove any ambiguity.

REACTION EQUATIONS The alignment and spacing is the same for all typed equations. The plus and the arrow have the standard space before and after. Typit key bars are available for the typing of arrows. A ruler should be used for arrows that are to be drawn.

$$4GeX_4 + 3Co_2(CO)_8 \xrightarrow{THF} 4X_3GeCo(CO)_4 + 2CoX_4 + 8CO$$

$$2GeCl_4 + 3Co_2(CO)_8 \xrightarrow{THF} 2Cl_2Ge[Co(CO)_4]_2 + 2CoX_2 + 8CO$$

$$CH_3GeI_3 + 2Na^+Co(CO)_4{}^- \xrightarrow{THF} (CH_3)IGe[Co(CO)_4]_2 + 2NaI$$

When an equation must be carried over to a second line or more than two lines, select the arrow as the breaking point.

$$Ni(NH_2CH_2CH_2CO_2)_2 + NH_2{}^- \longrightarrow$$

$$[Ni(NHCH_2CH_2CO_2)(NH_2CH_2CH_2CO_2)]^- + NH_3$$

$$[\,\mathrm{Ni(NHCH_2\,CH_2\,CO_2\,)(NH_2\,CH_2\,CH_2\,CO_2\,)}\,]^- + \mathrm{NH_2}^- \longrightarrow$$

$$[\,\mathrm{Ni(NHCH_2\,CH_2\,CO_2\,)_2}\,]^{2-} + \mathrm{NH_3}$$

Words, chemical symbols, or abbreviations may appear above and below other symbolism, and above and below arrows. Center this "explanatory notation" on the pattern or on the arrow.

$$2\mathrm{H_2O} \xrightarrow[\text{energy}]{\text{electric}} 2\mathrm{H_2}\uparrow + \mathrm{O_2}\uparrow$$

$$2\mathrm{KClO_3} \xrightarrow{\ \mathrm{MnO_2}\ } 2\mathrm{KCl} + 3\mathrm{O_2}\uparrow$$

LINE BONDS Typit key bars are available for single, double, and triple bonds between chemical symbols typed in formulas and equations. A line bond has no space before or after but is typed as close as possible to each chemical symbol. If line bonds are to be drawn they should be at least 4 mm, for they must not be confused with minus or equal signs. The proper letters must be under or on top of each other and the lines must be connected to the proper letters.

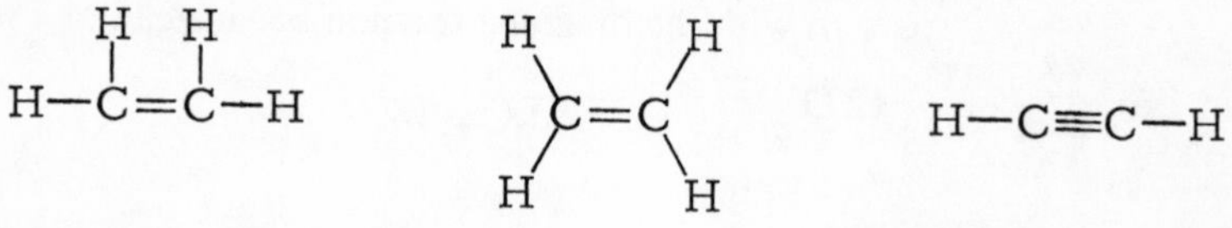

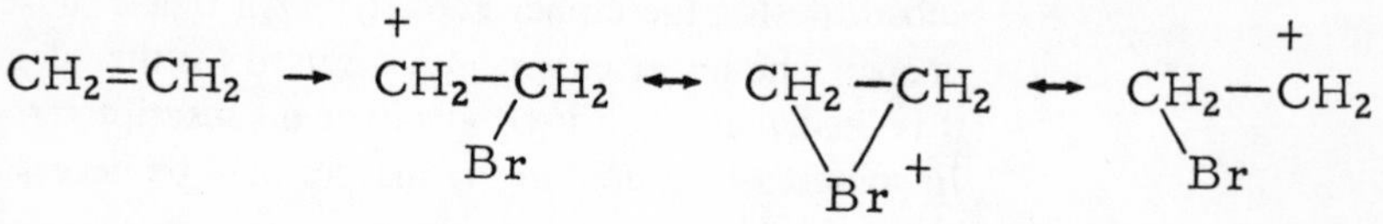

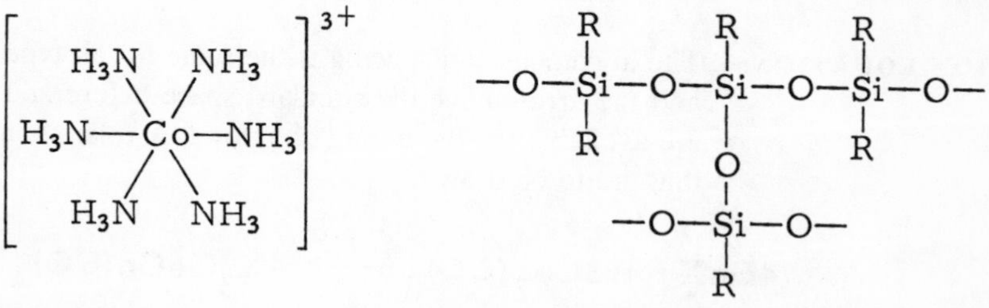

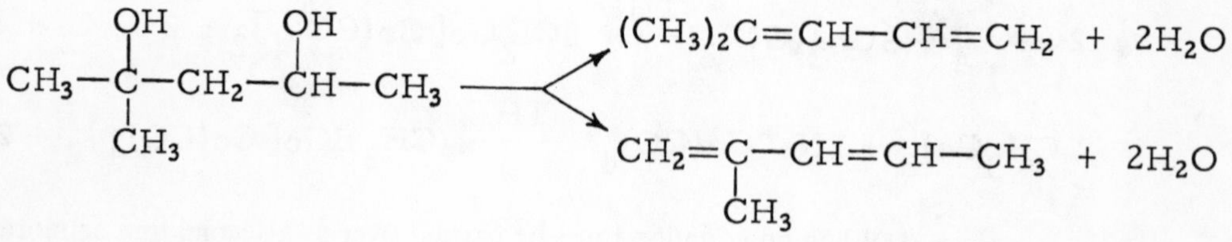

STRUCTURAL FORMULAS Displays of structural formulas are treated as illustrations (see p 65). Occasionally a relatively simple graphic display of an organic structure may be traced or drawn within the text. A drafting template should be used as a tracing guide (see footnote on p 102). The figure is usually drawn on the copy after all typing of chemical symbols has been completed.

Formula numbers, centered below the lowest part of a formula, should be typed well below the diagram so that they do not conflict with any chemical symbolism. These numbers are printed in boldface Arabic so that in the manuscript they must be underscored by a wavy line.

4

5

6

Equations—The starting place in typing an equation, a fraction, or almost any pattern is called the "main line." The major symbols (=, +, -, >, <, etc.), the equation number, punctuation, and parentheses and brackets should be typed on this line. The required pattern is then typed either above or below this level.

Fractions—Complex fractions should be typed with a horizontal bar. The fraction bar is made with the underscore key and is exactly as long as the longer term. The smaller pattern is then centered on this fraction bar.

$$\log \left[\frac{(k_{1c}/k_{1t})_1}{(k_{1c}/k_{1t})_2} \right] = \frac{\Delta E}{2.303R} \left[\frac{1}{T_2} - \frac{1}{T_1} \right]$$

$$\frac{1}{G(H_2) - 3.4} = \frac{1}{G_{e^-solv}} + \frac{1.}{G_{e^-solv}} \frac{k_1[N_2O]}{k_9[H^+]}$$

Notations—The *summation symbol* Σ and the *product symbol* Π must be drawn. These symbols are also available in dry transfer lettering (see p 68). The upper limits (above the symbol) and the lower limits (below the symbol) are typed.

$$i_m = -i \sum_{k=1}^{m-1} \alpha_{km} v_k \qquad \prod_{k=0}^{m-1} (1 - k \frac{m}{r})$$

When the summation (or product) appears in text paragraphs, the limits are shifted to the *right* above and below, thus

$$\prod_{-\infty}^{\infty}, \text{ and } \sum_{n=1}^{\infty}$$

The *integral symbol* $\int$ should slant a little to the right. The lower limits are typed below the line to the right of the symbol on a level with the lower curve of the symbol. The upper limits are then typed above the line and one or more spaces to the right of the first character in the lower limit.

$$\ln \underline{N_1} = -\int_{\underline{N_1}=1}^{\underline{N_1}=\underline{N_1}} \underline{N_2} \ d \ln (\underline{N_2}/\underline{N_1})$$

Exponentials may be typed either as $\underline{e}(\quad)$ or $\exp(\quad)$

For example: $\gamma + \underline{e}^{-\underline{i}(\underline{E_1}^2\underline{a}/2\delta\underline{i})} = 0$

$$\gamma + \exp[-\underline{i}(\underline{E_1}^2\underline{a}/2\delta_{\underline{i}})] = 0$$

When a pattern is too complicated to be typed as a superscript to "e," enclose the entire pattern in parentheses or brackets, and type it as a pattern spaced along and from the main line.

$$\exp\left\{\frac{\pi\underline{i}}{2}\left[(\underline{d}-1)(\underline{b}+\underline{ad}+\underline{c})+(\underline{a}-1)(\underline{c_1}-\underline{c})\right]\right\} = 1$$

Parentheses and *brackets* are used for separating parts of an equation. Letters are typed *without* space when they immediately precede or follow a parenthesis or bracket.

$$\underline{h} = \underline{f}[(\underline{A}-\underline{i})(\underline{A}+\underline{i})\underline{i}_{\underline{h}}]\underline{z} \qquad\qquad \underline{u} = \underline{F}[\underline{x}-(\underline{u}+\underline{c})\underline{t}]$$

Expressions containing the *radical sign* $\sqrt{}$ should be typed and drawn with care.

$$+\sqrt{\frac{\underline{a}(\underline{s}-\underline{b})(\underline{s}-\underline{c})}{\underline{k}}} \qquad\qquad \beta(\underline{t}) = \frac{1}{(3\beta\sqrt[3]{\underline{t_2}})(1+\sqrt[3]{\underline{t}_{\underline{q}}})^2}$$

Ellipsis dots are *exactly* three periods which indicate that certain quantities are known but omitted. Each dot is separated from its neighbors by one space. Raise the ellipsis dots for mathematical symbols, but not for punctuation.

$$\underline{f} = \alpha_0\underline{x}^{\underline{n}} + \underline{a}_1\underline{x}^{\underline{n}-1} + \cdot\ \cdot\ \cdot\ + \alpha_{\underline{n}}, \ \ldots$$

$$\underline{C}_1^{\underline{x}} \cdot\ \cdot\ \cdot\ \underline{C}_{\underline{r}}^{\underline{x}} = 1 \qquad\qquad \underline{C}_1^{\underline{x}} = 1,\ \ldots,\ \underline{C}_{\underline{r}}^{\underline{x}} = 1$$

A colon depicts *ratio*. $\underline{B}{:}\beta = \underline{pf}{:}\underline{pi}$

The exclamation point is used for a *factorial sign*. Simply combine a period and single quote to form this notation.

$$(\underline{n}+1)! \qquad\qquad \underline{t} - \frac{\alpha^2}{2!}$$

For *dot notation* directly above letters or symbols, type periods above letters as follows:

$$\underline{\dot{R}} \qquad\qquad \underline{\ddot{x}}_2\ \ddot{\pi}$$

SUMMARY OF EQUATION SPACING

HORIZONTAL (Use of Space Bar)

ONE SPACE	Each side of a mathematical sign on main line of equation, text, and display
	Each side of a summation, integral, product, min, max, lim, and so forth
	Each side of ellipsis dots
	Each side of trigonometric and logarithmic terms
	Each side of built-up fraction
	Each side of differential pair
	Between two fractions on main line
NO SPACE	In any part of superscript and subscript pattern
	Each side of a mathematical sign in denominator and numerator of fraction
	Each side of colon used for ratio
	Between closing parenthesis mark and next character
	Between end of equation and closing punctuation
	In any part of limits to summation, product, and integral
	In any part of lower limits to min, max, lim, inf, and so forth
	In any part of superscript pattern to "e"
	After a mathematical sign that immediately follows an equal sign
	Between any character and its own superscript and subscript
	Between back-to-back parentheses, brackets, and braces
	Between character and parenthesis or bracket
	Between "exp" and opening parenthesis or bracket
	Between members of differential pair
	Between character and factorial sign
	Between character and primes
MULTIPLE SPACE	Separating displayed equation and its parenthetical expression
	Separating groups of displayed equations on single line

VERTICAL (Hand-turns from Main Line)

ONE HALF HAND-TURN ABOVE	To superscript in text or display
	To lowest member of superscript of "e"
	To lowest character in numerator of fraction
	To horizontal fraction bar
	To limits of summation, products, integral in text
ONE HAND-TURN ABOVE	To super-superscript
	To superscript that has a subscript
	To upper limits of summation, product, integral in display
	To superscript of "e" that has a subscript
ONE HALF HAND-TURN BELOW	To subscript in text or display
	To lower limits of summation, product, integral in text
ONE HAND-TURN BELOW	To sub-subscript
	To subscript that has a superscript
	To highest character in denominator of fraction
	To lower limits of integral in display
ONE AND ONE HALF HAND-TURNS BELOW	To lower limits of summation and product in display
	To highest character of square root in denominator
	To limits pattern below min, max, lim, inf, and so forth
THREE HAND-TURNS ABOVE AND BELOW	Separating text paragraphs and displayed equations
	Separating individual displayed equations
	Separating turnover lines of a continued displayed equation
	Separating series of displayed equations

Appendix 5

PREFERRED SPELLING

A uniform style in journals is highly desirable for terms having more than one universally established spelling form. Uniformity of spelling within each paper is imperative.

The following list gives the preferred spelling for some words and expressions that are frequently troublesome to authors.

absorbance
aerobic
aging
air-dried (adj)
air dry (verb)
amine (RNH_2)
ammine (NH_3 complex)
ampoule
analog
aqua regia
asymmetry
audiofrequency
autoxidation
Avogadro

bacitracin
Beckmann thermometer
Beilstein
Bragg scattering (X-ray
   scattering from a crystal)
Büchner funnel
buildup (noun)
build up (verb)
buret
butanol, 1-butanol
  (not *n*-butanol)
butyl alcohol,
  n-butyl alcohol
by-product

cannot
catalog
clear-cut (adj)
coauthor
codistilled
condensable
conductometric
coordination
coworker

Darzens reaction
data (pl)
datum (sing)
deamido- (not desamido-)
deoxy- (not desoxy-)
desalination
desiccator
deuterium, deuterated
  (deuterio in naming
   compounds)

disc (biological)
discernible
disk (nonbiological)
distil
disubstituted
downfield
Dri-Film
drybox
Dry Ice

electropositive
eluate
eluent

far-infrared
filtrable
first-order reaction
flowsheet
fluorine
fluoroborate
formulas
free radical (noun)
free-radical (adj)

gauge
Geiger-Müeller tube
glasslike
Gouy
gray
Grignard

half-life
hemoglobin
hemolyzate
homolog
Hunsdiecker reaction

inflection
infrared
in vacuo (never "in vacuum,"
  but "under vacuum" is
  preferred)
ion-exchange (adj)
isooctane

Kekulé

labeled
large-scale extraction
laser
leveling
line width

liquefy
luster
lysate

media (plural of *medium*
except when meaning is
middle)
Mendeleev
methyl Cellosolve
methyl orange
midpoint
Millipore
mixture melting point
Mössbauer effect

near-ultraviolet
nonaqueous

oven-dried

per cent
percentage
pharmacopeia
phosphorus
pipet
pipetted
programming

radiofrequency
reexamine
reform (to amend)
re-form (to form again)
refractive indices
repellent
rotamer

side arm (noun)
side-arm (adj)

side chain (noun)
siphon
sizable
spectrophotometer
square-planar
steam bath
steam-distil (verb)
steam distillation (noun)
stepwise
sulfate
sulfonic
sulfur
syrup

test tube (noun)
test-tube (adj)
thermostated
Tollens reagent

ultraviolet
un-ionized
upfield

VandenHeuvel
van der Waals
viewpoint
Vigreux

water bath
wave function
wavelength
wave number
worthwhile

X-irradiation
X-ray
X-Ray (at start of sentence)

Appendix 6

NOTES ON GRAMMATICAL USAGE

The following pages point out some grammatical constructions that seem to be especially troublesome to the writer of technical material. These notes are not a complete treatment of the subjects; points singled out here are illustrative but are not necessarily more important than others that have been omitted. Authors who may need more information should turn to one of the many excellent texts available (see also references on p 117).

Subject-verb relationships—Two constructions that offer special hazards are 1) sentences in which the subject is really plural but grammatically singular, and 2) sentences with relative clauses. The following examples and comments may be helpful:

"Either of these solvents is satisfactory."

Since "either" is singular, "is" must be used instead of "are." *Neither, one, each, everyone, everybody, anyone, anybody* also take singular verbs.

"Either the apparatus or the original samples
were contaminated."

With an "either-or" or "neither-nor" construction, the verb must agree with that part of the subject nearest it.

> "One of the many experiments that were outlined was not completed."

The relative pronoun "that "refers to "experiments" and hence the verb "were" is plural.

> "This is one of those structures that are often confused."

The verb is plural because "that" refers to "structures."

Some collective nouns may take either a singular or plural verb, depending upon the sense of the statement. Examples: *contents, couple, dozen, group, majority, number, pair, variety.* When the author means the group as a whole, the collective noun takes a singular verb; when the author means the individuals of the group, the noun takes a plural verb.

> "A number of the flasks were broken."
> "The number of flasks that exploded was large."
> "The contents of the test tube was withdrawn."
> "Five grams of the isotope was added." (as a quantity)
> "Five grams of the isotope were added." (as individual units)

"Series" takes a singular verb.

> "A series of tests was run to determine the strength of the alloy."

"Data" should *not* be used as a collective, singular noun with a singular verb. "Data" is the plural of "datum" and therefore should take a plural verb.

> "The data are included in Table II."

Indefinite subjects such as *some, all, half,* take a plural verb when the real subject referred to is plural, but a singular verb if the real subject is singular.

> "Some of the instruments have been recalibrated."

Though plural in form, subjects representing sums, rates, measurements, quantities as a unit take a singular verb.

> "Six hours was spent on that report."
> "Three centimeters is more than one inch."

DANGLING CONSTRUCTIONS Phrases and clauses in which modifying words and phrases do not refer clearly to the word modified should be avoided. Modifiers must be placed so that the meaning of the statement is unmistakably clear.

> *Dangling:* "Having heated the mixture, a white precipitate appeared."
> *Corrected:* "A white precipitate appeared after the mixture was heated."
> *Misleading:* "When filtered a small amount of acid-insoluble material was removed from the acidic solution."
> *Corrected:* "The acidic solution was filtered to remove a small amount of acid-insoluble material."

FRAGMENTARY CONSTRUCTIONS Omission of a necessary verb auxiliary will cause fragmentary construction within the sentence.

> *Wrong:* "The tubes were stoppered and placed in a water bath, and the *temperature raised* by 5° increments."
> *Corrected:* "The tubes were stoppered and placed in a water bath, and the *temperature was raised* by 5° increments."

The second part of a comparison must not be omitted.

Incomplete: "The new method is more accurate."

Corrected: "The new method is more accurate than the one originally recommended."

Comparisons suggested by "different" and "differently" must be completed.

Incomplete: "The apparatus was different in design."

Corrected: "The apparatus was different in design from that reported by Jones."

Note that in the above example "different than" would be incorrect.

SUBORDINATION It is inefficient to express two ideas of unequal importance by means of equal or coordinate constructions. Subordination in sentence structure means showing by the structure of the sentence that one of the ideas expressed is less important than another.

Original: "This value is determined by actual measurement and is 25 volts."

Revised: "This value, best determined by actual measurement, is 25 volts."

Original: "A large volume of available process data includes several patents and gives details of the process and reactor."

Revised: "A large volume of available process data, including several patents, gives details of the process and reactor."

PARALLELISM Logic and orderliness demand the use of the same grammatical pattern for the expression of a series of roughly equal ideas.

Original: "The description was both accurate and it was easy to read."

Revised: "The description was both accurate and readable."

The need for parallelism is particularly noticeable in formal lists and in tables.

RESTRICTIVE AND NONDEFINING CLAUSES The relative pronouns "that" and "which" should not be used interchangeably. *That* is a defining pronoun and is used to introduce restrictive clauses. These clauses are essential to the meaning of the sentence.

"The reactions that were carried out in an
inert solvent gave very low yields."

Which is often nondefining and is used best to introduce nonrestrictive clauses. These clauses are loose modifiers that add descriptive but not limiting details and are not essential to the basic meaning of the sentence.

"The results, which are summarized in Table
III, show that quantum yield is essentially constant over the range studied."

Note that restrictive modifiers are not set off by commas but nondefining or nonrestrictive clauses must always be set off by commas.

In addition to faulty constructions certain stylistic flaws are likely to be confusing. Words and expressions should be chosen carefully to convey the correct meaning.

Use *while* only in the temporal sense meaning, "during (or at) the same time that" and not as a substitute for *but, although,* or *whereas.*

Do not say: "The *gluco* compound was not changed further by boiling sodium methoxide while the *manno* compound began to show a slight reaction."

Say, rather: "On addition to boiling sodium methoxide solution the *gluco* compound was unchanged, but the *manno* compound showed a slight reaction."

Do not say: "While the same technique was used, the mixture did not dissolve."

Say, rather: "Although the same technique was used, the mixture did not dissolve."

Do not say: "The sample (or compound, etc.) contained *x* counts/min."

Say, rather: "The radioactivity of the sample was *x* counts/min."

Do not say: "The activity applied on the column was . . ."

Say, rather: "The sample containing *x* units of radioactivity was applied to the column."

Do not say: "This compound was reacted with . . ."

Say, rather: "This compound was allowed to react with . . ." or ". . . was treated with . . ." or "was added to . . ."

Do not say: "Samples, planchettes, chromatographs, etc., were counted." The *radioactivity* is counted, in counts/min.

Do not say: "The per cent of silicon was found to be abnormally low."

Say, rather: "The percentage of silicon was abnormally low."

Do not use: the word *parameter* for factor, component, value, constant, etc. A parameter is a mathematical concept and has a very specific meaning.

Accuracy, precision—*Accuracy* refers to the discrepancy between the true value and the result obtained by measurement. *Precision* refers to the agreement among repeated measurements of the same quantity.

Adjust, calibrate—*Adjust* is now and then confused with *calibrate*. Adjustments or changes—usually slight ones—may be made without even hinting at calibration. *Calibration* suggests the determination of exact gradations, as of a measuring device.

Affect, effect—*Affect* is the verb; *effect,* the noun—in most usages. *Affect* means to change or modify; *effect* is the result of something. *Effect* may be used as a verb to mean *put into effect*. Correct: "This change will not affect system operation. The effect, in short, will be nil."

Alternate, alternative—*Alternate* means reciprocal, occurring or succeeding by turns; an *alternative* offers two things, one of which must be chosen, as the alternative of using an aqueous or a nonaqueous solvent.

Apparent, obvious, evident—That which is *apparent* is open to view; that which is *obvious* is unavoidably clear, so clear as to need no explaining; that which is *evident* is demonstrable by facts or evidence.

Assure, insure, ensure—To *assure* is to confirm or to make (one) certain; to *insure* is to assure against a loss by a contingent event, on certain stipulated conditions or at a given rate, *i.e.,* to underwrite; to *ensure* is to make sure, certain, safe, to guarantee.

Compare, contrast—In most usage *compare* means to point out similarities and differences, but *contrast* should be reserved for the latter meaning. A few writers restrict the meaning of *compare* to pointing out likenesses alone.

Compose, comprise, consist—These words are not exactly synonymous and may not always be used interchangeably. Consult your dictionary. For example:

A solution *is composed of* solute ions and solvent.

A solution *comprises* solute ions and solvent.

A sodium chloride solution *consists of* sodium ions, chloride ions, and solvent.

Continual, continuous—The former means over and over again at short intervals; the latter means occurring without ceasing.

Distinguish, differentiate—The former means to recognize (and point out) those aspects of something that mark its separate identity; the latter means to point out the difference between two things.

Enable, permit—To *enable* is to provide power or competency to be or do something; to *permit* is to allow or authorize.

Fewer, less—*Fewer* applies to individual units; *less* to quantity. It is not best usage, therefore, to speak of less people being in attendance than formerly.

Flammable, inflammable—Both words have the same meaning. However, *flammable* is preferred.

Imply, infer—To *imply* means to express an opinion or to present a fact indirectly without being blunt or outspoken; to *infer* means to draw a tentative conclusion and to suggest it as a hypothesis.

Partially, partly—The antonyms suggest the distinction to be made in these words: partially—completely; partly—wholly. Although for many uses the two may be synonymous, *partly* is preferred.

Portion, proportion, part—A *portion* is a part of a whole; a *proportion* is the relation of one portion to another, or to the whole, or of one thing to another, as respects magnitude, quantity, or degree. *Proportion* is often misused for *part;* it should be reserved to express a comparative relation between things or magnitudes.

Principal, principle—These two words are frequently confused even though the distinction in meaning is commonly understood; the trouble is basically one of spelling forms. *Principal* means (in technical usage) *main, chief, most important; principle* means a physical truth or an accepted code of conduct. *Principle* is always a noun; *principal* is an adjective in technical writing.

Utilize, use—As a verb, *use* has the same meaning as utilize, since nothing is gained in precision of meaning by using the longer word, the shorter words *use, used, using* should be used in place of *utilize, utilized, utilizing.*

Various, varying—*Various* is an adjective meaning different, changeable, inconstant; *varying,* from the verb *to vary,* means modifying, altering in form, appearance, substance, position.

Appendix 7

JOURNAL ABBREVIATIONS

Literature references to technical journals should follow the system of abbreviations as given in the *Guide for Abbreviating Periodical Titles* and the *Chemical Abstracts List of Periodicals* (see p 72).

The following list*consists of the recommended abbreviations for the chemistry and chemical engineering journals covered by *Chemical Titles*, a publication of the Chemical Abstracts Service. Since journal titles and their abbreviations are printed in *italics*, they must be underlined in the manuscript.

e.g.,

Journal title	Abbreviation as printed	Abbreviation as it should appear in manuscript
Annalen der Chemie	*Ann. Chem.*	*Ann. Chem.*
Annales de Chimie (Paris)	*Ann. Chim.* (Paris)	*Ann. Chim.* (Paris)
Bulletin of the Chemical Society of Japan	*Bull. Chem. Soc. Jap.*	*Bull. Chem. Soc. Jap.*
Doklady Akademii Nauk SSSR	*Dokl. Akad. Nauk SSSR*	*Dokl. Akad. Nauk SSSR*

A.I.C.H.E. (Amer. Inst. Chem. Eng.) J.
Abh. Deut. Akad. Wiss. Berlin, Kl. Chem., Geol. Biol.
Acta Biochim. Pol.
Acta Biol. Acad. Sci. Hung.
Acta Biol. Acad. Sci. Hung., Suppl.
Acta Biol. Med. Ger.
Acta Biol. Med. Ger., Suppl.
Acta Chem. Scand.
Acta Chim. Acad. Sci. Hung.
Acta Crystallogr.
Acta Endocrinol. (Copenhagen)
Acta Endocrinol. (Copenhagen), Suppl.
Acta Histochem.
Acta Histochem., Suppl.
Acta Met.
Acta Pathol. Microbiol. Scand.
Acta Pathol. Microbiol. Scand., Suppl.
Acta Pharm. Hung.
Acta Pharm. Hung., Suppl.
Acta Pharmacol. Toxicol.
Acta Pharmacol. Toxicol., Suppl.
Acta Phys. Acad. Sci. Hung.
Acta Physiol. Scand.
Acta Physiol. Scand. Suppl.
Acta Pol. Pharm.
Acta Vitaminol. (Milan)
Advan. Catal.
Advan. Chem. Eng.
Advan. Cryog. Eng.
Aerosol Age
Agr. Biol. Chem. (Tokyo)
Agressologie
Agrochimica
Agrokem. Talajtan
Agrokem. Talajtan, Suppl.
Agron. J.
Air Eng.
Air Water Pollut.
Amer. J. Bot.
Amer. J. Enol. Viticult.
Amer. Mineral
Amer. Physiol.
Amer. J. Sci.
An. Acad. Brasil. Cienc.
An. Bromatol. (Madrid)
An. Real Soc. Espan. Fis. Quim., Ser. A

An. Real Soc. Espan. Fis. Quim., Ser. B
Anal. Biochem.
Anal. Chem.
Anal. Chim. Acta
Analyst (London)
Angew. Chem.
Ann. Chim. (Paris)
Ann. Chim. (Rome)
Ann. Inst. Pasteur
Ann. Inst. Pasteur, Suppl.
Ann. Intern. Med.
Ann. N. Y. Acad. Sci.
Ann. Pharm. Fr.
Ann. Phys. (Leipzig)
Ann. Phys. (N. Y.)
Ann. Phys. (Paris)
Antibiotiki
Appl. Microbiol.
Appl. Spectrosc.
Aptech. Delo
Arch. Biochem. Biophys.
Arch. Eisenhuettenw.
Arch. Environ. Health
Arch. Int. Pharmacodyn. Ther.
Arch. Int. Physiol. Biochim.
Arch. Pathol.
Arch. Pharm. (Weinheim)
Arch. Sci. Physiol.
Ark. Kemi
Arm. Khim. Zh.
Arzneim.-Forsch.
At. Energ.
Atti Accad. Naz. Lincei, Rend., Cl. Sci. Fis. Mat. Nat.
Aust. J. Agr. Res.
Aust. J. Biol. Sci.
Aust. J. Chem.
Azerb. Khim. Zh.
Ber. Bunsenges. Phys. Chem.
Biochem. Biophys. Res. Commun.
Biochem. J.
Biochem. Pharmacol.
Biochem. Pharmacol., Suppl.
Biochem. Z.
Biochemistry
Biochim. Appl.
Biochim. Biophys. Acta
Biofizika
Biokhimiya
Biophys. J.
Biopolym., Symp.

Biopolymers
Biotechnol. Bioeng.
Bitamin
Blood
Bochu Kagaku
Bol. Soc. Quim. Peru
Boll. Chim. Farm.
Boll. Sci. Fac. Chim. Ind. Bologna
Boll. Sci. Fac. Chim. Ind. Bologna, Suppl.
Boll. Soc. Ital. Biol. Sper.
Brennst.-Chem.
Brit. Chem. Eng.
Brit. J. Appl. Phys.
Brit. J. Cancer
Brit. J. Nutr.
Brit. J. Pharmacol. Chemother.
Bul. Inst. Politeh. "Gheorghe Gheorghiu-Dej" Bucuresti
Bull. Acad. Pol. Sci., Ser. Sci. Biol.
Bull. Acad. Pol. Sci., Ser. Sci. Chim.
Bull. Chem. Soc. Jap.
Bull. Inst. Chem. Res., Kyoto Univ.
Bull. Inst. Chem. Res., Kyoto Univ., Suppl. Issue
Bull. Soc. Chim. Belges
Bull. Soc. Chim. Biol.
Bull. Soc. Chim. Fr.
Bull. Soc. Fr. Ceram.
Bull. Soc. Fr. Ceram., Suppl.
Bull. Soc. Fr. Mineral. Cristallogr.
Bull. Soc. Roy. Sci. Liege
Bum. Prom.
Bunseki Kagaku
Bunseki Kagaku, Shinpo Sosetsu
Byull. Eksp. Biol. Med.
C. R. Acad. Bulg. Sci.
C. R. Acad. Sci., Paris, Ser. A,B
C. R. Acad. Sci., Paris, Ser. C
C. R. Acad. Sci., Paris, Ser. D
C. R. Soc. Biol.
Can. J. Biochem.
Can. J. Chem.
Can. J. Chem. Eng.
Can. J. Microbiol.
Can. J. Phys.
Can. J. Physiol. Pharmacol.

*In alphabetical order by abbreviations.

114

Can. J. Plant Sci.
Can. J. Soil Sci.
Cancer (Philadelphia)
Cancer Res.
Carbohyd. Res.
Carbon (Oxford)
Cereal Chem.
Cesk. Farm.
Chem. Anal. (Warsaw)
Chem. Ber.
Chem. Brit.
Chem. Commun.
Chem. Eng. (London)
Chem. Eng. (N. Y.)
Chem. Eng. Progr.
Chem. Eng. Progr., Symp. Ser.
Chem. Eng. Sci.
Chem. Ind. (London)
Chem.-Ing.-Tech.
Chem. Listy
Chem. Pharm. Bull. (Tokyo)
Chem. Process Eng.
Chem. Prum.
Chem. Rev.
Chem. Stosow., Ser. A
Chem. Stosow., Ser. B
Chem. Tech. (Berlin)
Chem. Weekbl.
Chem.-Ztg., Chem. App.
Chem. Zvesti
Chemist-Analyst
Chemotherapia
Chim. Anal. (Paris)
Chim. Chron.
Chim. Ind. (Milan)
Chimia
Circ. Res.
Circ. Res., Suppl.
Clin. Chem.
Clin. Chim. Acta
Clin. Pharmacol. Ther.
Clin. Sci.
Cobalt
Collect. Czech. Chem. Commun.
Colloq. Int. Centre Nat.
  Rech. Sci.
Combust. Flame
Comp. Biochem. Physiol.
Contr. Eng.
Corros. Anti-Corros.
Corros. Sci.
Corrosion
Croat. Chem. Acta
Cryogenics
Curr. Sci.
Denki Kagaku
Dokl. Akad. Nauk Arm. SSR
Dokl. Akad. Nauk Azerb. SSR
Dokl. Akad. Nauk Beloruss. SSR
Dokl. Akad. Nauk SSSR
Dokl. Akad. Nauk Tadzh. SSR
Dokl. Akad. Nauk Uzb. SSR
Dopov. Akad. Nauk Ukr. RSR
Econ. Geol.
Eesti NSV Tead. Akad.
  Toim., Biol. Seer.
Eesti NSV Tead. Akad.
  Toim., Fuus.-Mat.
  Tehnikatead. Seer.
Eiyo to Shokuryo
Electrochem. Technol.
Electrochim. Acta
Elektrokhimiya
Endeavour
Endocrinol. Jap.
Endocrinology
Endokrinologie
Environ. Sci. Technol.
Enzymologia
Erdoel Kohle, Erdgas, Petrochem.
Eur. Polym. J.
Exp. Cell Res.
Exp. Cell Res., Suppl.
Exp. Mol. Pathol.
Exp. Mol. Pathol., Suppl.
Exp. Parasitol.
Experientia
Experientia, Suppl.
Farbe Lack
Farm. Zh. (Kiev)
Farmacia (Bucharest)
Farmaco, Ed. Prat.
Farmaco, Ed. Sci.
Farmakol. Toksikol.
Fed. Proc.
Ferment. Spirt. Prom.
Fette, Seifen, Anstrichm.
Fiz.-Khim. Mekh. Mater.
Fiz. Metal. Metalloved.
Fiz. Tverd. Tela
Fiziol. Rast.
Fiziol. Zh. (Kiev)
Fiziol. Zh. SSSR
Food Technol. (Champaign, Ill.)

Fresenius' Z. Anal. Chem.
Fuel (London)
G. Biochim.
Gazov. Prom.
Gazz. Chim. Ital.
Gen. Comp. Endocrinol.
Gen. Comp. Endocrinol., Suppl.
Genshiryoku Kogyo
Geochim. Cosmochim. Acta
Geokhimiya
Geol. Zh.
Gidroliz. Lesokhim. Prom.
Gig. Sanit.
Glas. Hem. Drus., Beograd
Hakko Kogaku Zasshi
Hakko Kyokaishi
Health Phys.
Helv. Chim. Acta
Helv. Phys. Acta
Helv. Phys. Acta, Suppl.
Helv. Physiol. Pharmacol. Acta
Helv. Physiol. Pharmacol. Acta,
  Suppl.
Hikaku Kagaku
Hoppe-Seyler's Z. Physiol. Chem.
Hua Hsueh
Hua Hsueh Hsueh Pao
Igaku to Seibutsugaku
Immunochemistry
Ind. Chim. Belge
Ind. Eng. Chem.
Ind. Eng. Chem., Fundam.
Ind. Eng. Chem., Process
  Des. Develop.
Ind. Eng. Chem., Prod. Res.
  Develop.
Indian J. Biochem.
Indian J. Chem.
Indian J. Exp. Biol.
Indian J. Pharm.
Indian J. Pure Appl. Phys.
Indian J. Technol.
Inform. Quim. Anal. (Madrid)
Inorg. Chem.
Inorg. Nucl. Chem. Lett.
Inst. Gas Eng. J.
Inst. Mining Met., Trans./Sect. A
Inst. Mining Met., Trans./Sect. B
Inst. Mining Met., Trans./Sect. C
Instrum. Contr. Syst.
Int. J. Appl. Radiat. Isotopes
Int. J. Heat Mass Transfer
Int. J. Neuropharmacol.
Int. J. Radiat. Biol.
Int. Z. Vitaminforsch.
Inzh.-Fiz. Zh.
Iron Steel Eng.
Israel J. Chem.
Izv. Akad. Nauk Azerb. SSR,
  Ser. Fiz.-Tekh. Mat. Nauk
Izv. Akad. Nauk Kaz. SSR,
  Ser. Khim.
Izv. Akad. Nauk SSSR, Metal.
Izv. Akad. Nauk SSSR, Ser. Biol.
Izv. Akad. Nauk SSSR, Ser. Fiz.
Izv. Akad. Nauk SSSR, Ser. Geol.
Izv. Akad. Nauk SSSR, Ser.
  Khim.
Izv. Akad. Nauk Turkm. SSR,
  Ser. Biol. Nauk
Izv. Akad. Nauk Turkm. SSR,
  Ser. Fiz.-Tekh., Khim.
  Geol. Nauk
Izv. Akad. Nauk Uzb. SSR,
  Ser. Fiz.-Mat. Nauk
Izv. Sib. Otd. Akad. Nauk
  SSSR, Ser. Biol.-Med. Nauk
Izv. Sib. Otd. Akad. Nauk
  SSSR, Ser. Khim. Nauk
Izv. Timiryazev. Sel'skokhoz.
  Akad.
Izv. Vyssh. Ucheb. Zaved.,
  Chern. Met.
Izv. Vyssh. Ucheb. Zaved., Fiz.
Izv. Vyssh. Ucheb. Zaved.,
  Khim. Khim. Tekhnol.
Izv. Vyssh. Ucheb. Zaved.,
  Neft Gaz
Izv. Vyssh. Ucheb. Zaved.,
  Pishch. Tekhnol.
Izv. Vyssh. Ucheb. Zaved.,
  Tsvet. Met.
J. Agr. Food Chem.
J. Agr. Sci.
J. Amer. Ceram. Soc.
J. Amer. Chem. Soc.
J. Amer. Leather Chem. Ass.
J. Amer. Leather Chem. Ass.,
  Suppl.
J. Amer. Oil Chem. Soc.
J. Amer. Water Works Ass.
J. Antibiot. (Tokyo), Ser. A
J. Antibiot. (Tokyo), Ser. B
J. Appl. Chem. (London)

J. Appl. Phys.
J. Appl. Phys., Suppl.
J. Appl. Physiol.
J. Appl. Polym. Sci.
J. Ass. Offic. Anal. Chem.
J. Atheroscler. Res.
J. Bacteriol.
J. Basic. Eng.
J. Biochem. (Tokyo)
J. Biol. Chem.
J. Catal.
J. Cell Biol.
J. Cell Comp. Physiol.
J. Cell. Comp. Physiol., Suppl.
J. Chem. Doc.
J. Chem. Educ.
J. Chem. Eng. Data
J. Chem. Phys.
J. Chem. Phys., Suppl.
J. Chem. Soc., A
J. Chem. Soc., B
J. Chem. Soc., C
J. Chem. U. A. R.
J. Chim. Phys.
J. Chin. Chem. Soc. (Taipei)
J. Chromatogr.
J. Clin. Endocrinol. Metab.
J. Clin. Invest.
J. Colloid Interfac. Sci.
J. Dairy Sci.
J. Dent. Res.
J. Econ. Entomol.
J. Electroanal. Chem.
J. Electrochem. Soc.
J. Endocrinol.
J. Eng. Ind.
J. Exp. Med.
J. Food Sci.
J. Gen. Appl. Microbiol. (Tokyo)
J. Gen. Appl. Microbiol. (Tokyo),
  Suppl.
J. Gen. Microbiol.
J. Gen. Physiol.
J. Heat Transfer
J. Heterocycl. Chem.
J. Histochem. Cytochem.
J. Immunol.
J. Indian Chem. Soc.
J. Infec. Dis.
J. Inorg. Nucl. Chem.
J. Inst. Brew.
J. Inst. Fuel
J. Inst. Metals Bull. Met. Rev.
J. Inst. Petrol.
J. Inst. Water Eng.
J. Iron Steel Inst. (London)
J. Lab. Clin. Med.
J. Label. Compounds
J. Less-Common Metals
J. Lipid Res.
J. Med. Chem.
J. Mol. Biol.
J. Mol. Spectrosc.
J. Nat. Cancer Inst.
J. Neurochem.
J. Nucl. Energy, Parts A/B
J. Nucl. Mater.
J. Nutr.
J. Nutr., Suppl.
J. Oil Colour Chem. Ass.
J. Opt. Soc. Amer.
J. Org. Chem.
J. Organometal. Chem.
J. Paint Technol.
J. Parasitol.
J. Pathol. Bacteriol.
J. Pharm. Belg.
J. Pharm. Belg., Suppl.
J. Pharm. Pharmacol.
J. Pharm. Pharmacol., Suppl.
J. Pharm. Sci.
J. Pharmacol. Exp. Ther.
J. Photogr. Sci.
J. Phys. (Paris)
J. Phys. (Paris), Suppl.
J. Phys. Chem.
J. Phys. Chem. Solids
J. Phys. Soc. Jap.
J. Phys. Soc. Jap., Suppl.
J. Physiol. (London)
J. Physiol. (Paris)
J. Physiol. (Paris), Suppl.
J. Polym. Sci., Part A-1
J. Polym. Sci., Part A-2
J. Polym. Sci., Part B
J. Polym. Sci., Part C
J. Prakt. Chem.
J. Proc. Inst. Chem. (India)
J. Quant. Spectrosc. Radiat.
  Transfer
J. Res. Nat. Bur. Stand., A
J. S. Afr. Chem. Inst.
J. Sci. Food Agr.
J. Sci. Ind. Res.

J. Sci. Instrum.
J. Soc. Cosmet. Chem.
J. Soc. Dyers Colour.
J. Soc. Leather Trades' Chem.
J. Soil Sci.
J. Theor. Biol.
J. Virol.
J. Vitaminol. (Kyoto)
Justus Liebigs Ann. Chem.
Kagaku Kogaku
Kami-pa Gikyoshi
Kauch. Rezina
Kaut. Gummi, Kunstst.
Kernenergie
Khim. Geterotsikl. Soedin.
Khim. Ind. (Sofia)
Khim. Neft. Mashinostr.
Khim. Prir. Soedin.
Khim. Prom.
Khim. Tekhnol. Topl. Masel
Khim. Volokna
Kinet. Katal.
Klin. Wochenschr.
Kobunshi Kagaku
Kogyo Kagaku Zasshi
Koks Khim.
Kolloid-Z. Z. Polym.
Kolloid. Zh.
Kozh.-Obuv. Prom.
Kristallografiya
Lab. Delo
Latv. PSR Zinat. Akad. Vestis
Leather Sci. (Madras)
Leder
Liet. TSR Mokslu Akad.
    Darb., Ser. B
Life Sci. (Oxford)
Lipids
Listy Cukrov.
Lubric. Eng.
Magy. Kem. Foly.
Magy. Kem. Lapja
Makromol. Chem.
Mater. Sci. Eng.
Mech. Eng.
Melliand Textilber.
Metab., Clin. Exp.
Metall (Berlin)
Metalloved. Term. Obrab. Metal.
Metallurgia
Microchem. J.
Mikrobiol. Zh. (Kiev)
Mikrobiologiya
Mikrochim. Acta
Mineral. Mag.
Mitt. Geb. Lebensmittelunters.
    Hyg.
Mod. Plast.
Mol. Cryst.
Mol. Pharmacol.
Mol. Phys.
Monatsh. Chem.
N. Z. J. Sci.
Nagoya Kogyo Gijutsu Shikensho
    Hokoku
Nature
Naturwissenschaften
Naunyn-Schmiedebergs Arch.
    Pharmakol. Exp. Pathol.
Neftekhimiya
Nichidai Igaku Zasshi
Nippon Gomu Kyokaishi
Nippon Kagaku Zasshi
Nippon Mokuzai Gakkaishi
Nippon Naibunpi Gakkai Zasshi
Nippon Nogei Kagaku Kaishi
Nippon Yakurigaku Zasshi
Nucl. Instrum. Methods
Nucl. Instrum. Methods, Suppl.
Nucl. Phys., A
Nucl. Phys., B
Nucl. Sci. Eng.
Nuovo Cimento, A
Nuovo Cimento, B
Nuovo Cimento, Suppl.
Oesterr. Chem.-Ztg.
Ogneupory
Opt. Spektrosk.
Ovo Butsuri
Package Eng.
Paint Varn. Prod.
Paperi Puu
Papier
Perfum. Essent. Oil Rec.
Period. Polytech., Chem.
    Eng. (Budapest)
Petro/Chem. Eng.
Pharm. Acta Helv.
Pharm. Prax. (Berlin)
Pharm. Zentralh. Deut.
Pharmazie
Phil. Mag.
Photochem. Photobiol.
Photogr. Sci. Eng.

Phys. Chem. Glasses
Phys. Fluids
Phys. Lett.
Phys. Rev.
Phys. Rev. Lett.
Phys. Status Solidi
Physica
Physiol. Plant.
Phytochemistry
Phytopathology
Plant Physiol.
Plant Physiol., Suppl.
Plant Soil
Plast. Massy
Plast. Technol.
Pochvovedenie
Polym. Eng. Sci.
Polymer
Postepy Biochem.
Prib. Tekh. Eksp.
Prikl. Biokhim. Mikrobiol.
Probl. Endokrinol. Gormonoter.
Proc. Indian Acad. Sci., Sect. A
Proc. Indian Acad. Sci., Sect. B
Proc. Nat. Acad. Sci., India,
    Sect. A
Proc. Nat. Acad. Sci., India,
    Sect. B
Proc. Nat. Acad. Sci. U. S.
Proc. Phys. Soc.
Proc. Roy. Soc., Ser. A
Proc. Roy. Soc., Ser. B
Proc. Soc. Exp. Biol. Med.
Prod. Eng.
Progr. Theor. Phys. (Kyoto)
Progr. Theor. Phys. (Kyoto),
    Suppl.
Przem. Chem.
Psychopharmacologia
Pure Appl. Chem.
Quart. Rev. (London)
Radiat. Res.
Radiat. Res., Suppl.
Radiochim. Acta
Radiokhimiya
Rec. Chem. Progr.
Rec. Trav. Chim. Pays-Bas
Rev. Chim. (Bucharest)
Rev. Inst. Fr. Petrole Ann.
    Combust. Liquides
Rev. Mod. Phys.
Rev. Phys. Chem. Jap.
Rev. Port. Quim.
Rev. Roum. Biochim.
Rev. Roum. Phys.
Rev. Sci. Instrum.
Ric. Sci.
Riechst., Aromen, Koerperp-
    flegem.
Rika Gaku Kenkyusho Hokoku
Rocz. Chem.
Rubber Age (N. Y.)
Sakh. Prom.
Scand. J. Clin. Lab. Invest.
Scand. J. Clin. Lab. Invest.,
    Suppl.
Sci. Cult. (Calcutta)
Sci. Ind. Photogr.
Sci. Pap. Inst. Phys. Chem.
    Res. (Tokyo)
Sci. Rep. Res. Inst., Tohoku
    Univ., Ser. A
Sci. Sinica (Peking)
Science
Seibutsu Butsuri Kagaku
Seikagaku
Sekiyu Gakkai Shi
Sen-i Gakkaishi
Soil Sci.
Soil Sci. Soc. Amer. Proc.
Soobshch. Akad. Nauk Gruz. SSR
Sov. Geol.
Spectrochim. Acta
Sperimentale
Staerke
Stain Technol.
Stal'
Steklo Keram.
Steroids
Steroids, Suppl.
Stud. Cercet. Biochim.
Stud. Cercet. Chim.
Stud. Cercet. Fiz.
Stud. Cercet. Met.
Suomen Kemistilehti, A
Suomen Kemistilehti, B
Svensk Kem. Tidskr.
Svensk Papperstidn.
Talanta
Tappi
Tekst. Prom. (Moscow)
Teor. Eksp. Khim.
Teploenergetika
Teplofiz. Vys. Temp.

Tetrahedron
Tetrahedron Lett.
Tetrahedron, Suppl.
Text. Res. J.
Theor. Chim. Acta
Therapie
Tidsskr. Kjemi, Bergv. Met.
Tohoku J. Exp. Med.
Toxicol. Appl. Pharmacol.
Toxicol. Appl. Pharmacol., Suppl.
Tr. Khim. Khim. Tekhnol.
Trans. Brit. Ceram. Soc.
Trans. Faraday Soc.
Trans. Inst. Chem. Eng.
Trans. Inst. Metal Finish.
Trans. Inst. Rubber Ind.
Trans. Met. Soc. AIME (Amer.
    Inst. Mining, Met., Eng.)
Trans. N. Y. Acad. Sci.
Trans. N. Y. Acad. Sci., Suppl.
Tsvet. Metal.
Tsitologiya
Ukr. Biokhim. Zh.
Ukr. Fiz. Zh.
Ukr. Khim. Zh.
Usp. Fiz. Nauk
Usp. Khim.
Usp. Sovrem. Biol.
Uzb. Biol. Zh.
Uzb. Khim. Zh.
Vac. Microbalance Tech.
Vestn. Akad. Nauk Kaz. SSR
Vestn. Leningrad. Univ., Ser.
    Fiz. Khim.
Vestn. Mosk. Univ., Ser. II.
Vestn. Mosk. Univ., Ser. VI.
Vestsi Akad. Navuk Belarus.
    SSR, Ser. Biyal. Navuk
Vestsi Akad. Navuk Belarus.
    SSR, Ser. Fiz.-Tekh. Navuk
Virology
Vop. Med. Khim.
Vop. Pitan.
Vvsokomol. Soedin.
Water Wastes Eng.
Werkst. Korros.
Yakugaku Zasshi
Yogyo Kyokai Shi
Yukagaku
Yuki Gosei Kagaku Kyokai Shi
Z. Anorg. Allg. Chem.
Z. Chem.
Z. Kristallogr.
Z. Lebensm.-Unters. Forsch.
Z. Metallk.
Z. Naturforsch., A
Z. Naturforsch., B
Z. Pflanzenernaehr., Dueng.,
    Bodenk.
Z. Phys.
Z. Phys. Chem. (Frankfurt am
    Main)
Z. Phys. Chem. (Leipzig)
Z. Vitamin-, Hormon- Ferment-
    forsch.
Z. Zuckerind.
Zap. Vses. Mineral. Obshchest.
Zavod. Lab.
Zellst. Papier
Zh. Anal. Khim.
Zh. Eksp. Teor. Fiz.
Zh. Eksp. Teor. Fiz., Pis'ma
    Redaktsiyu
Zh. Fiz. Khim.
Zh. Mikrobiol., Epidemiol.
    Immunobiol.
Zh. Nauch. Prikl. Fotogr.
    Kinematogr.
Zh. Neorg. Khim.
Zh. Obshch. Biol.
Zh. Obshch. Khim.
Zh. Org. Khim.
Zh. Prikl. Khim.
Zh. Prikl. Spektrosk.
Zh. Strukt. Khim.
Zh. Tekh. Fiz.
Zh. Vses. Khim. Obshchest.

SELECTED REFERENCES

In addition to the references mentioned in the text, the following works are recommended.

LANGUAGE B. EVANS AND C. EVANS, *A Dictionary of Contemporary American Usage,* Random House, New York, N. Y., 1957.

H. W. FOWLER, *A Dictionary of Modern English Usage,* 2nd ed, revised by E. A. Gowers, Oxford University Press, New York, N. Y., 1965.

M. NICHOLSON, *Dictionary of American-English Usage,* Oxford University Press, New York, N. Y., 1957.

GENERAL TECHNICAL WRITING L. F. FIESER AND M. FIESER, *Style Guide for Chemists,* Reinhold Publishing Corp., New York, N. Y., 1960.

R. FLESCH, *ABC of Style,* Harper and Row Publishers, Inc., New York, N. Y., 1965.

J. FOSTER, JR., *Science Writer's Guide,* Columbia University Press, New York, N. Y., 1962.

W. J. GENSLER AND K. D. GENSLER, *Writing Guide for Chemists,* McGraw-Hill Book Co., New York, N. Y., 1961.

E. A. GOWERS, *Plain Words, Their ABC's,* Alfred A. Knopf, Inc., New York, N. Y., 1957.

R. GUNNING, *The Technique of Clear Writing,* McGraw-Hill Book Co., New York, N. Y., 1952.

F. H. RHODES, *Technical Report Writing,* McGraw-Hill Book Co., New York, N. Y., 1961.

M. E. SKILLIN AND R. M. GAY, *Words into Type,* Appleton-Century-Crofts, Inc., New York, N. Y., 1964.

W. STRUNK, JR. AND E. B. WHITE, *The Elements of Style,* The Macmillan Co., New York, N. Y., 1959.

A Manual of Style, University of Chicago Press, Chicago, Ill., 1949.

STATISTICS, TABLES, AND GRAPHS J. A. ANDERSON, "The Preparation of Illustrations and Tables," *Trans. Amer. Ass. Cereal Chem.,* **3** (2), 74 (1945). (Reprints available from the American Association of Cereal Chemists, St. Paul, Minn.)

W. H. BEYER, Ed., *Handbook of Tables for Probability and Statistics,* The Chemical Rubber Co., Cleveland, Ohio, 1966.

M. G. NATRELLA, "Experimental Statistics," National Bureau of Standards Handbook 91, Washington, D. C., 1963.

C. F. SCHMID, *Handbook of Graphic Presentation,* The Ronald Press Co., New York, N. Y., 1954.

W. A. WILDHACK, R. C. POWELL, AND H. L. MASON, "Accuracy in Measurements and Calibrations," National Bureau of Standards Technical Note 262, Washington, D. C., 1965.

A. G. WORTHING AND J. GEFFNER, *Treatment of Experimental Data,* John Wiley and Sons, Inc., New York, N. Y., 1943.

W. J. YOUDEN, *Statistical Methods for Chemists,* John Wiley and Sons, Inc., New York, N. Y., 1951.

W. J. YOUDEN, "Statistical Design," reprints from *Ind. Eng. Chem.,* American Chemical Society Publications, Washington, D. C.

Manual of Tabular Presentation, U. S. Bureau of the Census, Washington, D. C., 1949.

MISCELLANEOUS   A. A. BLAKER, *Photography for Scientific Publication, A Handbook,* W. H. Freeman and Co., San Francisco, Calif., 1965.

T. W. CHAUNDY, P. R. BARRETT, AND C. BATEY, *The Printing of Mathematics,* Oxford University Press, New York, N. Y., 1954.

N. J. DUNFORD, *A Handbook for Technical Typists,* Gordon and Breach, Inc., New York, N. Y., 1964.

A. R. STAFFORD AND B. J. CULPEPPER, *The Science-Engineering Secretary: a guide to procedure, usage, and style,* Prentice-Hall, Inc., Englewood Cliffs, N. J., 1963.

Index

A

B

C

D

E

F

G

H

I

J

K

L

M

N

O

PRIMARY PUBLICATIONS OF THE AMERICAN CHEMICAL SOCIETY

Journal	Issues per Year	Sections	Editor[1]	Address
ACCOUNTS OF CHEMICAL RESEARCH	12[2]	Concise Reviews Special Features Reports on Scientific Meetings	Dr. Joseph F. Bunnett Division of Natural Sciences	University of California Santa Cruz, California 95060
ADVANCES IN CHEMISTRY SERIES[3]		Symposia	Mr. Robert F. Gould*	American Chemical Society Washington, D. C. 20036
ANALYTICAL CHEMISTRY	13[4]	Articles Notes Correspondence Aids for Analytical Chemists Book Reviews[5] Special Features	Dr. Herbert A. Laitinen* Department of Chemistry and Chemical Engineering	University of Illinois Urbana, Illinois 61801
BIOCHEMISTRY	12	Articles Accelerated Publications	Dr. Hans Neurath Department of Biochemistry	University of Washington Seattle, Washington 98105
CHEMICAL REVIEWS	6	Reviews	Dr. Harold Hart Department of Chemistry	Michigan State University East Lansing, Michigan 48823
ENVIRONMENTAL SCIENCE AND TECHNOLOGY	12	Articles Communications Reviews Correspondence Book Reviews[5] Special Features	Dr. James J. Morgan* W. M. Keck Laboratory of Environmental Health Engineering	California Institute of Technology Pasadena, California 91109
INDUSTRIAL AND ENGINEERING CHEMISTRY	12	Reviews Correspondence Book Reviews[5] Special Features	Mr. David E. Gushee*	American Chemical Society Washington, D. C. 20036
I&EC FUNDAMENTALS	4	Articles Communications Correspondence Experimental Technique	Dr. Robert L. Pigford* Department of Chemical Engineering	University of California Berkeley, California 94720
I&EC PROCESS DESIGN AND DEVELOPMENT	4	Articles Communications Correspondence	Dr. Hugh M. Hulburt* Department of Chemical Engineering	Northwestern University Evanston, Illinois 60201
I&EC PRODUCT RESEARCH AND DEVELOPMENT	4	Articles Correspondence	Mr. Rodney N. Hader* (Acting Editor)	American Chemical Society Washington, D. C. 20036
INORGANIC CHEMISTRY	12	Articles Notes Correspondence	Dr. Edward L. King Department of Chemistry	University of Colorado Boulder, Colorado 80302

Journal	No.	Sections	Editor	Address
JOURNAL OF AGRICULTURAL AND FOOD CHEMISTRY	6	Articles Communications	Dr. Philip K. Bates*	363 Seventeenth Street Santa Monica, California 90402
JOURNAL OF THE AMERICAN CHEMICAL SOCIETY	26	Articles Communications Book Reviews[5]	Dr. Marshall D. Gates, Jr. Department of Chemistry	University of Rochester Rochester, New York 14627
JOURNAL OF CHEMICAL DOCUMENTATION	4	Articles News and Notes Book Reviews[5]	Dr. Herman Skolnik Hercules Research Center	Hercules Incorporated Wilmington, Delaware 19809
JOURNAL OF CHEMICAL AND ENGINEERING DATA	4	Articles	Dr. Bruce H. Sage* Chemical Engineering Laboratory	California Institute of Technology Pasadena, California 91104
JOURNAL OF MEDICINAL CHEMISTRY	6	Articles Notes New Compounds Book Reviews[5]	Dr. Alfred Burger Department of Chemistry	University of Virginia Charlottesville, Virginia 22901
MACROMOLECULES	6[2]	Articles Communications Reviews	Dr. Field H. Winslow Polymer Research & Development Department	Bell Telephone Laboratories Murray Hill, New Jersey 07971
THE JOURNAL OF ORGANIC CHEMISTRY	12	Articles Notes	Dr. Frederick D. Greene Department of Chemistry	Massachusetts Institute of Technology Cambridge, Massachusetts 02139
THE JOURNAL OF PHYSICAL CHEMISTRY	12	Articles Notes Communications	Dr. Frederick T. Wall Building 255 Camp Matthews	University of California San Diego, P. O. Box 109 La Jolla, California 92037
			Dr. F. C. Tompkins[6] The Faraday Society	6 Gray's Inn Square London, W. C. 1, England

OTHER PUBLICATIONS OF THE AMERICAN CHEMICAL SOCIETY AND ITS DIVISIONS

ACS MONOGRAPHS
Dr. F. Marshall Beringer
Department of Chemistry
Polytechnic Institute of Brooklyn
Brooklyn, New York 11201

CHEMICAL &
ENGINEERING NEWS
Mr. Gordon H. Bixler
American Chemical Society
Washington, D. C. 20036

CHEMISTRY
Dr. O. Theodor Benfey
Chemistry Department
Earlham College
Richmond, Indiana 47375

JOURNAL OF
CHEMICAL EDUCATION
Dr. William T. Lippincott
Department of Chemistry
Ohio State University
Columbus, Ohio 43210

RUBBER CHEMISTRY
& TECHNOLOGY
Dr. Edward M. Bevilacqua
Research Center
U.S. Rubber Company
Wayne, New Jersey 07470

[1] Manuscripts should be directed to the editor at the address shown except where the editor's name is followed by an asterisk *

In these cases, manuscripts should be addressed:
Editor,
(name of journal),
1155 Sixteenth Street, N. W.,
Washington, D. C. 20036.

[2] Starts publication in January 1968.

[3] Although not a journal this publication is part of the primary literature.

[4] A special issue, "Annual Review," is published each April.

[5] Copies of new books dealing with areas of chemistry of interest to the readers may be sent to the editor. Reviewers are selected by the editors.

[6] Manuscripts for The Journal of Physical Chemistry originating in the British Isles, Europe, or Africa should be sent to The Faraday Society.